Hiss and Tell
The Memoirs

SATAN

Hiss and Tell
The Memoirs

SATAN

Ebury Press
London

Published by Ebury Press
Division of The National Magazine Company Ltd
Colquhoun House
27–37 Broadwick Street
London W1V 1FR

First impression 1988
Copyright © 1988 Jeremy Pascall
Illustrations © 1988 Martin Brown

ISBN 0 85223 766 9

Edited by Miren Lopategui
Designed by Harry Green

Typeset by Textype Typesetters, Cambridge
Printed and bound in Great Britain
at The Bath Press, Avon

A MESSAGE FROM THE AUTHOR

IF YOU ARE TEMPTED TO STEAL THIS BOOK...
GO AHEAD!

Just pick it up, slip it into your pocket or bag and
walk out of the shop.
Take it from a friend's shelf.
Or pretend to borrow it with no intention of
returning it.

Go on, do it! Be a devil!*

* The publishers would like to dissociate themselves from this
flagrant incitement to theft. In fact, the publishers would like to
dissociate themselves from everything contained in this book. We
only agreed to publish it because we felt that, in a free society, even
The Author has a right to put his point of view, however dishonest,
twisted and perverse.
And because we hope to make lots and lots of lovely lucre.

DEDICATION

This book is dedicated to Pride, Anger, Envy, Lust,
Gluttony, Greed and Sloth.
And so am I.
Why not join me and indulge in the
Seven Delightful Sins?
Think of the fun we could have together!*

* Discover the joy of the Eighth Delightful Sin later in the book!

PUBLISHER'S WARNING

While we took every effort to check the facts in this book, it must be remembered that The Author is the most accomplished liar in the history of the universe.

Nothing contained in this book should be believed.

Except this statement.

And, frankly, even this is not entirely true because we made very little effort to check the facts. Mainly because the first editor who worked with The Author disappeared under unusual and suspicious circumstances and was last seen dancing stark naked on Salisbury Plain, sacrificing a chicken by biting its head off.

And the second editor...well, suffice it to say that the second editor who had the temerity to question The Author on the veracity of the text suddenly changed his job. And his form. Having no vacancies in the company for a goat, however talented, we reluctantly let him go. But not, sadly, before he had eaten part of the manuscript and most of the Managing Director's furniture.

The third and last editor decided, wisely in our opinion, not to challenge The Author on any of his so-called facts. She struck up a close working relationship with The Author and, as a result, is alive and well in the Seychelles, living very comfortably on the £500,000 she embezzled from this company.

BY THE SAME AUTHOR

'Arson for Profit and Pleasure'

'The Good Hell Guide'

'Incest – Fun for all the Family'

'Hell's Kitchen – 100 Tempting Barbecue Dishes'
(including Devilled Crab, Angels on Horseback –
made with real angels and horses – and Soul,
fried, grilled and meunière)

'The Living Dead – Biographies of Six Famous
Belgians' (Well, all right, Three Quite Well
Known Belgians)

'The Boy's Big Book of Torture'

'The Girl's Big Book of Bonking'

'The Joy of Sin'

'The Joy of Goats'

'The Country Diary of an Edwardian Ladykiller'

'My Animals and Other Family'

'Paradise Lost – What Really Happened in Heaven'

'Paradise Mislaid – What Really Happened
to Atlantis'

'Work for Idle Hands – A Manual
of Black Arts and Crafts'

(All recommended by *Witch* Magazine.)

Sintroduction

Sintroduction

**G**REETINGS!

Allow me to introduce myself. I am Satan. Or, if you prefer, The Devil, Lucifer, The Prince of Darkness, The Evil One, The Serpent, Beezlebub, Mephistopheles, Old Nick ...I answer to all these. Although I'm not too happy about the last. Nick, I may be, but old? I'm considerably younger than Him Upstairs. Compared to The Great Fraud, as I call Him, I'm a teenager. All right, I've been around a long time but I don't consider myself elderly. What I say is, you're as old as you feel; or as old as the woman you feel! (Or the man or goat you feel. I think it's silly to be prejudiced about these matters. My philosophy is: don't knock it until you've tried it. Or, to put it another way, suck it and see. And, of course, vice versa.)

I really do object to being depicted as old. How many other men of my age regularly perform fifteen despicable acts, destroy the careers of six public figures, corrupt a dozen Catholic priests and fornicate with a variety of living creatures each and every day? And all before breakfast!

11

SATAN

I have my pride, you know. In fact, Pride is my favourite sin. All right, it's not as much fun as Lust or Gluttony or Greed but, of course, I take enormous pride in my lustfulness and nobody, but nobody, is as gluttonous as me. However, when it comes to Greed I have to acknowledge that lawyers may have the edge.

But I digress. It's one of my little failings, one of my many little failings along with unpunctuality, untidiness, meanness and rampant kleptomania. Of course, I also have many big failings – like sexual depravity, genocide and not using a hankie when I sneeze – which you'll learn about in due course.

To return to my subject: you probably know me best as Satan. But my real name is Kevin.

Kevin! Yes, that's my Chris...ooops! nearly had to wash my mouth with soap and brimstone...my forename. Can't stand it myself, I'd have preferred something with a bit more nobility about it. Typical, isn't it, that when G** – I can't even bring myself to type His name – when The Great Fraud, was handing out names to His other archangels, they were called Gabriel, Raphael, Uriel and Zadkiel, but not me. I got Kevin. Which just goes to prove He never liked me. I sometimes wonder what would have happened if He'd called me something decent like Azrael. Perhaps I wouldn't have had such a chip on my shoulder and things would have turned out differently. Maybe I'd have stayed in Heaven and helped Him out, doing odd jobs like polishing halos, tuning harps and clipping the wings of cherubim who tried to fly before they could walk. How boring! I've no regrets about the existence I've led, so much more fun than Heaven. Mind you, even Belgium is more fun than Heaven. Or would be, if it didn't have so many Belgians.

So now you know my real name and the first of my big secrets is out – just one of the many I will reveal in these pages.

I know some people are surprised that I've taken so long to write my memoirs. There are many reasons for this, not least the fact that I've been waiting for a publisher to come up with enough lucre. Of course, over the eons others have tried to persuade me to jot down my life story and I've frequently been tempted. But, you see, I'm so easily tempted. In fact, as I once rather wittily commented, I can resist anything except temptation![1]

Being so prone to temptation, I've always signed the contract, taken the lucre and run off with it without writing a word. Serves them right for trusting me and anyway what can they do about it? Sue me? It would never stand up in court, especially as most of the lawyers in the world work for me – you've heard of devil's advocates, haven't you? I really admire lawyers, brilliant people who lie, cheat and steal you blind and it's all absolutely legal! They're people after my own heart and, indeed, wallet. What a blow for Him Upstairs! The Great Fraud may have formulated the laws, but the people who bend, twist and pervert them are good chums of mine. I've reserved a very special place in Hell for lawyers.

The reason that I'm finally dipping my nib in vitriol and putting pen to paper is that at last someone has come up with enough incentive for me to do it. True, there was a problem when I told the publishers that I wanted to be paid in either (i) their souls or (ii) virgins. Caused a lot of consternation because it seems that most publishers have already sold the first and none of the second could be found working in their trade. In the end I settled for truck-loads of lucre.[2]

Not that I need the lucre, you understand. I'm probably the richest being in history. Compared to me, your average billionaire is a beggar and I made J. Paul Getty look like a pauper. And, indeed, I made him look like a porpoise. Didn't you ever wonder why he was so glum? People used to comment that he had all that money and yet he looked as miserable as

---

1. *Publisher's note:* Most sources ascribe that remark to Oscar Wilde. It would seem that The Author has plagiarized this line but, as he points out, 'Not for nothing am I known as The Bubonic Plagiarist! I only steal from the best. Unless I'm getting new ideas for wickedness and then I only steal from the very worst.'

2. The publishers would like to point out that we are paying The Author the usual fee for writing this book plus, of course, his royalties. Or, rather, Satanies. And we'd further like to add that in the matter of greed, unscrupulousness and treachery, The Author is no worse than the average literary agent. In fact, he has rather more integrity than most.

sin. I take exception to that. I'm here to tell you that sin isn't miserable, it's deliciously pleasurable.

The trouble with Getty was that he didn't know how to enjoy his money and when I offered him some tips – like using it to destabilize the economies of Third World countries – he spurned me. So in revenge I gave him the face of a fish. (Him Upstairs later stole this idea and used it on Andrew Lloyd Webber. The reason the poor blighter looks like he does is because he failed to pay The Great Fraud His deities for 'Jesus Christ Superstar'. You know, He has a vicious streak that even I have to admire, grudgingly.)

But even being so rich doesn't mean that I don't want more lucre. I want it all! Never believe people when they tell you that money doesn't buy you happiness, that's just a rumour put around by the wonderfully and disgustingly wealthy to stop the rest of you getting your hands on their's. Sadly, however, it is true that you can't take it with you, otherwise I'd have had all the lovely lucre they brought down when they joined me in Hades. (Incidentally, I've disproved that nonsense put about by Him Upstairs when He said that a rich man can't pass through the eye of a needle. Of course he can. If you chop him up into little pieces – preferably while he's still alive – put him in a blender, squish him round until he's liquefied and then dribble him through the eye, drop by drop. A most enjoyable experiment!)[3]

Despite my enormous and insatiable greed, the lucre is not the main reason I've consented to write these memoirs. Frankly, during the last few years my company, Hades p.l.c., has suffered a few setbacks. For some reason there's been a nasty outbreak of piety in the world. This, of course, may just be the usual pendulum of trade. We did particularly well in the 'sixties and 'seventies – recruitment flourished with

3. When we pointed out to The Author that the Biblical text tells us that it is easier for a camel to pass through the eye of a needle than for a rich man to enter Heaven, he said, 'I've only read The Bible once and that was to check for any loopholes. And anyway, squishing a camel is not nearly as much fun as liquefying a bloated capitalist.' The publishers would like to warn young readers not to attempt this experiment for themselves as it is cruel, perverted and may cause irreparable damage to your mother's food blender.

enormously encouraging increases among the young and we ruthlessly exploited the growth area of capturing the souls of such trendy hedonists as actors and, particularly, rock stars who were falling into our hands at a tremendous rate. Oh, for those heady days of sex and drugs and rock and roll and sex and drugs and more sex! There was a time when you could hardly move down here without rubbing shoulders (and other far more interesting parts of the anatomy) with some pop superstar.

But since 1980 business hasn't been so good. Despite my worst efforts I've found that more and more people have been turning to the opposition, buying what The Great Fraud calls His 'fire insurance' – sign up with Him and He'll guarantee you won't enjoy the many and varied benefits of my own organization.

My firm's motto has always been 'Live Now, Pay Later', but His marketing boys have come up with a new campaign around the slogan 'Pray Now, Live For Ever' which, to my surprise and disappointment, has proved remarkably successful. Let's be hone...I mean, let's face it, we were caught unawares by the sheer number of Born Again Christians. In fact, it seems that there's one Born Again every minute, and to try to stem the flow I've decided to address you directly, to tell my story, to show you where you're going right and how much more pleasure you'll get if you go wrong.

So, read this book and enjoy it. And if at the end of it you don't want to follow me down the primrose path to eternal wickedness, let me just say: Have a lousy day. And remember what happend to the *Titanic*. That taught them to refuse me a free first-class cabin!

You know, I'm often accused of being a bad loser. And it's true. But to be fair, I'm also a very bad winner.

Satan

Chapter Twelve[4]
Not Quite The Beginning

am the most maligned being in history and, indeed, in prehistory given that I was around long before you shambling anthropoids first set your stumbling feet on The Earth. It's hard to believe, but The Great Fraud is actually proud of creating you ramshackle creatures! I mean, look at you! Pathetic, stringy things without a decent pair of horns or even a tail. Mind you, He did create you on the sixth day, so I suppose He must have run out of inspiration, not to mention spare parts which probably explains why you look like you were hastily and carelessly flung together from the left-over bits of other animals.

Still, I was pleased enough to see some human life, however inadequate. Don't forget that I was about my devilishly devious work eons before Adam and Eve first saw the light of day. And very welcome they were, at least to me, because, let's face it, before them there was very little fun for a Satanic being. How would you like to waste your time, charm and

4. This is, of course, Chapter One. The author can't resist exaggerating.

CHAPTER TWELVE

seductive talents trying to tempt rocks into the ways of wickedness? Or persuading lumps of wood to indulge in rampant sexual orgies? So, you see, Adam and Eve were literally Heaven-sent for me. But I digress again, I'll get around to the tru...no, I have trouble with that word too... the *real* story of Adam and Eve in my own bad time.

To return to the subject: ever since I pulled off my first successful temptation in the Garden of Eden, I have been reviled and vilified, pilloried and libelled; every misfortune, disaster and catastrophe has been blamed on me. I've been accused of everything from the destruction of Pompeii to causing the First World War.[5] Of every evil from the introduction of murder to the invention of nylon tights.

While I'm prepared to proudly admit my involvement in the first three, I can't accept the blame for tights; they were the creation of a deeply puritanical mind and have probably done more to set back my campaign for unbridled lust than anything since the chastity belt. That, at least, had a profitable spin-off for me; namely, a huge increase in professional lock-pickers. Although, of course, there were always those who wanted to take a short cut; I'm thinking of a passionate young swain called Rufus the Dickhead who decided to free his loved one from her confinement by attaching a charge of dynamite to her iron girdle. Gave her a terrific bang, but he had trouble explaining to her husband when he returned from the Crusades how she came to be buried in a very small envelope. In fact, he completely failed to come up with a convincing story. Unfortunately for him, the husband was a man of violent temper which explains how the swain subsequently became known as Rufus the Dickless.

There I go, digressing again. What I'm saying is that I've been getting a bad press since time immemorial and, of course, in *Time Immemorial*, the magazine for immortals, which has named me as its 'Evil Bastard of the Year' for 7,237,961,548 years running. I ask you, has any being ever had a worse reputation?

---

5. What a brilliant coup World War One was! Imagine me persuading two super-powers like Britain and Germany to plunge the Earth into global conflict. And all over Belgium!

SATAN

So, let's get one thing straight from the start: I love it! I revel in each and every slur. The more I'm accused, the more I enjoy it. You should see my scrapbooks – volume after volume of stories about me and not one good word to be found in my favour! In spare moments, when I'm not trying to lead you all towards Armageddon, I drool over the billions of reports of my despicable deeds! Do you realize that when asked, ninety out of a hundred ordinary mass murderers in the street claimed that I was their inspiration! Very flattering. The remaining ten said they had been motivated after hearing the voice of Him Upstairs ordering them to kill in His name. Gullible fools! Do they really think He'd talk to them? He's so high and mighty, He barely deigns to pass the time of day with His saints. And don't they realize that ventriloquism is one of my many talents!

Oh, I simply love being me, I wouldn't change myself for all the tea in China. Hang on, though...that's rather tempting. If you were also to throw in all the souls in China, we might have a deal. Although, of course, I'd instantly renege on it.

Yes, I *adore* being evil. Wickedness is so much more fun than piety. I've spent almost my entire existence enjoying every sin and transgression you can imagine and many hundreds more that your minuscule minds aren't capable of imagining. I've indulged myself in the pursuit of pleasure and wallowed in every physical gratification. There is nothing I haven't done, no sexual depravity I haven't experienced. (How many of you can boast of enjoying an active sexual relationship with a duckbilled platypus? And a homosexual relationship at that? Quite pleasurable it was too. But not as truly satisfying as doing something unspeakably depraved with a dead warthog. But enough of these nostalgic reminiscences about my past loves. Sometimes I think that I'm just a silly, sentimental old romantic.)

I've relished every moment of my misspent existence. And, being a generous man, I've always been willing to share my life-style with you. Yes, YOU. For example, why don't you put this book down for a moment and do something really naughty? Go on! It doesn't *have* to be arson or blood-letting (great fun in themselves, but they make a terrible mess of the carpet), it could be something simple to start with, like

CHAPTER TWELVE

scoffing a whole box of chocolates, drinking another bottle of wine or whipping your gerbil with barbed wire. Whatever it is, do it! You'll feel better for it afterwards. Believe me. Would I lie to you?[6]

The point I'm making is that you shouldn't believe everything you read about me. I'm not as bad as I'm made out to be. I'm much, much worse. I'm so irredeemably wicked that I make Adolf Hitler look like Mother Teresa.

That's how truly, utterly evil I am and the question many people ask is: have I always been evil? Was I created evil? Or did I just practise long and hard? To answer that I'll have to go right back to The Beginning...

---

6. Yes, of course, I would lie to you. It's my business, my craft, my art and my pleasure. But on the other hand, I'm such a practised liar that you can never be sure that I'm not lying when I say that I'd lie to you. The trouble is that when I say I'm lying to you, I am, in fact, telling the truth. But as I'm incapable of telling the truth, I must be lying. Oh, what intricate webs of deception I weave! Sometimes I even confuse myself.

Chapter Seven[7]
The Beginning

n the beginning was the Word and the Word was 'w********k' which is the rudest word in the whole universe. It is so rude that grown men have been known to spontaneously combust just at the sound of it. And grown women have been known to commit acts of gross sexual abandon with Christmas trees. That's how rude it is. And I was the very first person ever to utter the word. In fact, it was the first word I ever spoke when still just a seraphim and only knee high to a cockroach.[8]

7. This is, of course, Chapter Two. The Author is lying in an attempt to cause confusion.

8. For obvious reasons we are not able to print the word in full. The only time it has been written, in a medieval manuscript, was by a monk who was inscribing it on to parchment. As soon as he penned the last letter, his head exploded. The precise meaning of the word is unclear as it has never appeared in a dictionary. But we believe that a rough definition is: 'to derive sexual stimulation by using a porcupine as a suppository.' We would like to warn any children not to attempt this as it stunts the growth, causes blindness and may lead to madness. Apart from these effects on the porcupine, it won't do you any good either.

CHAPTER SEVEN

This, of course, was long, long before your Earth was created, when the universe was just a black void waiting to be filled. All that existed in those far-off days was Heaven. Well, The Great Fraud called it Heaven but the rest of us didn't think much of it. A dreary place, not much better than a shack, painted ditchwater brown and sludge green. We often used to complain about it, especially the plumbing which left a lot to be desired, like pipes, running water and a toilet seat. But The Great Fraud said it was Paradise compared to everything else, which was accurate considering there wasn't anything else.

In those dull days there was just Him Upstairs and His few archangels — Gabriel, Raphael, Uriel, Zadkiel and me, Tracie.[9]

He'd created us when He became bored whizzing about the utterly empty universe looking in vain for some place to hang out on a Saturday night where He could have a couple of beers, play a game of pool and listen to His favourite hymns on the jukebox. He decided He needed some companions with whom to share the so-called delights of Heaven, to be His disciples and pupils and to do the washing up.

We were the first beings He created and, though I say it myself, we were a damn fine looking bunch of ethereals. In our halos, enormous wings and spotless white frocks we positively glowed, so you can understand that we didn't take kindly to living in a slum. I mean, no sooner had you put on a clean frock in the morning and stepped outside than it was grubby and, remember, this was long before a really reliable biological washing powder came on the market.

Now, I'm not one to gossip. Well, of course, I *am* one to gossip, I mean who do you think put around the rumour about St Cecilia using a Great Dane as a vibro-massager? (Not to

9. All right, I lied when I said my name was Kevin, I was too embarrassed to reveal that I started my existence as Tracie. What sort of name is that? Especially for a boy? I still believe that He called me it out of spite. I protested to Him about it and pleaded with Him to change it, which reluctantly He did. Which is how I spent the next three millennia answering to the name of Rover.

No wonder I turned out as I did. You know what they say, give a god a bad name...

mention a Terrific Swede and a Really Buttock-Clenchingly Fantastic Norwegian.) And being one to gossip, I ask you, what sort of Supreme Being dresses His male archangels in frocks? Okay, so He called them kaftans, but does that explain why He insisted that we wore frou-frou bras, lace basques, suspender belts and silk stockings underneath them? I tell you, He's one weird old man. Look at the facts – has He ever been seen out with a woman? Never! Always going around with a bunch of men. And the only time He felt the need to procreate Himself, what happened? He got The Holy Ghost to do it for Him. I leave you to draw your own conclusions.

What else can I tell you about Heaven? The clothes were suspect, the plumbing was primitive, the accommodation was awful and the food was worse. We survived on a staple diet of nectar and ambrosia which have been greatly over-rated by scholars and poets who never had to eat the stuff. Nectar resembles mud-flavoured yogurt while ambrosia has the look and consistency of blotting paper but, sadly, doesn't taste half as nice. One of my first clashes with Him was about the menu.

When I complained, all He could say was: 'You've got ambrosia to eat and nectar to drink. What else do you want?'

So I said, 'What else have You got?'

'Nothing,' He said.

'Nothing? Why not?'

'Because there isn't anything else.'

'Well,' I said, 'why don't You create something?'

'Like what?'

'Like caviar,' I suggested.

'Caviar?' He boomed. 'What's caviar?'

'I don't know, but it's a nice word. Why don't you create something caviar-ish?'

'Like what?' He asked.

'I don't know. Like fishes' eggs, maybe?'

'You know, Rover,' He said. 'Sometimes you really disgust me. What sort of pervert would want to eat fishes' eggs?'

I explained it was just an idea off the top of my halo but He wouldn't have any of it. 'And furthermore,' He continued, 'what on Heaven are fishes?'

CHAPTER SEVEN

There He had me. 'I don't know what they are. I just thought of a word. "Fish", it sounds like something we could eat, so why don't You, in Your infinite omnipotence which You are constantly boasting about, create "fish" which we could eat? I mean, it doesn't *have* to be "fish", it could be... well, to pull another word out of the air...it could be "sofa". I don't care what it's called so long as it isn't nectar or bloody ambrosia.'

'Rover,' He shouted, 'I would remind you that I am God Almighty, Lord of the Universe, The Supreme Being and not a short-order cook.'

'All right,' I said, 'keep Your hair on.'

Now, that's where I got Him. He's very sensitive to any references about His hair. Or, rather, lack of it. What you don't realize is that He's completely bald. I expect you've seen all those portraits of Him with His long flowing locks – well, they're a con. What you don't know is He's wearing a wig. And a very unconvincing one. I mean, who does He think He's fooling with a snowy white beard and bright ginger hair? He really does look ludicrous. What a stroke I pulled when I persuaded Him to wear it!

Anyway, I eventually managed to goad Him into coming up with some alternative food. And the next day we all tucked into His latest creation – sand-flavoured pot noodles.

When we'd finished the meal, He said, 'So, what do you think of it?'

And Gabriel, being a grovelling little crawler, said, 'Verily, it is a feast and a banquet. Never has anyone dined on such exquisite fare.'

And Raphael, Uriel and Zadkiel – fearing for their jobs – all concurred. 'Verily, You have created the food of the Gods.'

And The Great Fraud turned to me and said, 'And what do you think, Rover?'

And I said, 'I think Verily is a stupid name for The Supreme Being and You should change it immediately. And while You're about it, You can change my name too.'

He waxed wrathful at this, saying, 'Verily is not My name!'

And the others said, 'Verily, Verily is *not* His name. Verily is a word we made up while you were washing your frock. It means "truly".'

And I thought that was typical of them, making up words behind my back just so they could win at Scrabble. But I said nothing, preferring to bide my time and plan my revenge.

Seeing my silence, The Great Fraud said, 'Stop sulking. If you don't like being called Rover, what name would you like?'

'I don't know. One like the others have. Something classy that ends in "iel".'

He thought for a moment and said, 'Very well. Let it be known that from this day hence Rover will be called Muriel.'

The others all laughed because in those days, when we were still making up names for things, 'Muriel' meant 'lavatory brush'. But I held my peace, knowing my time would come.

'So, Muriel,' said He, 'what do you think of my sand-flavoured pot noodles? Were they not delicious?'

'They were not delicious. They tasted like the inside of Gabriel's posing pouch.'

This caused great perturbation – especially to Gabriel who thought that none of us knew how he spent his evenings, standing in front of the mirror wearing nothing but his gold lamé pouch, flexing his muscles and saying, 'My but you're a good-looking hunk of angel!'

He and the others all shouted, 'Oh, Lord, do not listen to him. Believe us, Your sand-flavoured pot noodles are the greatest thing since sliced...since sliced whatjamacallit? Oooh, what was the name of that sliced thing You created the day before yesterday?'

And He said, 'Manure.'

And they all carolled, 'Verily, they are the greatest thing since sliced manure! And we'd like second helpings!'

He turned to me again, 'See, Muriel, everyone else likes My pot noodles.'

To which I replied, 'You may be The Lord of All Creation, The Supreme and Omnipotent Being, but you're a lousy cook. Personally, I'd prefer to eat my own intestines.'

And he glowered at me and spake. And when He spake, His voice was as thunder.

'I should have known it from the moment I created you, you're a trouble-maker.'

And the others all chorused: 'Yes! Muriel is a trouble-maker! Muriel is a trouble-maker!'

CHAPTER SEVEN

And then they said, 'What's "trouble"? Can you eat it? If so, will you make us some, Muriel?'

I replied, 'I don't know what "trouble" is, but when I find out I promise I'll make plenty of it for you.'

They all shouted 'Oh! Goody!'

But Himself spake not a word. He just glared, frowning furiously at me under His ginger wig.

'Oh, w********k it!,' I thought to myself, 'Why didn't I keep my mouth shut?'

And that was The End of The Beginning of The Beginning.

Chapter Thirteen[10]

The Middle of The Beginning

The next day we all sat down to our meal again. And after Himself had said grace – 'For what I am about to provide, may you all be truly grateful' – He said, 'I have made an important decision. I have decided that there will be no repeat of what happened yesterday. In future there will be no more arguments between us. Understand, Muriel?'

And I said, 'What happened yesterday was not an argument.'

And He said, 'Yes, it was!'

'No, it wasn't!'

'Was, too!'

'Wasn't!'

10. This is, of course, Chapter Three. Originally, The Author wanted every
     chapter to be Thirteen, 'because it's my favourite number, unlucky for
     most which makes it very lucky for me. My second favourite number is
     666 – the number of The Beast. Whenever I need something beastly
     done, I dial 666 and it comes running to do my diabolic bidding.'

CHAPTER THIRTEEN

'Was! Was! WAS!'

And I said, 'Look, what we had yesterday was a heated exchange of views in which we offered our opinions fully and frankly. What we're doing now is having an argument.'

'This is *not* an argument!'

'Yes it is!'

'No, it isn't!'

And I said, 'Yes it is, but there's no use arguing about it.'

'I am NOT arguing!'

'Yes, You are!'

'No I am NOT!'

'All right,' I said, 'Have it Your own way. But there's no point in getting hoity-toity just because You can't admit You're wrong.'

And He waxed wrathful again and declared, 'I am NEVER wrong! It is not possible for Me to be wrong, I am God Almighty, The Supreme and Perfect Being. I am utterly infallible. And if you don't shut up, I'll turn you into a toad. How would you like that?'

And I said, 'I'm not sure. What's a toad?'

'A toad?' He said.

'Yes, as You are The Supreme and Perfect Being, who can't get anything wrong, just tell me what a toad is.'

'Well, um, it's a large four-legged animal with a flowing mane and a long swishy tail. So there! Now, that's enough of that, let's eat!'

'Hear! Hear!,' said Gabriel, 'I'm starving!'

And the others agreed, saying, 'We're so hungry we could eat a toad!'

Himself served up the food. This time, instead of the miserable little portions we usually got, the table groaned under a huge dish covered with an enormous silver dome. Before He whipped off the dome, He said, 'This is My latest culinary masterpiece!' And with a flourish He revealed it to us.

We looked at it in awed silence, then we sniffed the aroma steaming off it and we prodded it with our forks. Truly we had seen nothing to compare with it. Eventually Gabriel broke the expectant hush.

'It's certainly very large.'

'Very large,' agreed Raphael.

'Now,' said Uriel, 'if I was asked for just one word to describe it, that word would, without any doubt, be "large".'

'Extraordinary you should say that,' chipped in Zadkiel, 'because, believe it or not, the first word that sprang to my mind when I saw it was "large".'

'Is that all you've got to say?' asked Himself.

'Well,' said Gabriel, 'we haven't actually tried it yet. Perhaps when we've tasted it we'll be able to say something else.'

So Himself carved us each a slice and placed it before us and one by one we tasted it.

'Well?' He demanded.

Again Gabriel was the first to speak. 'I can say without a shadow of doubt that in all my experience this is absolutely and unequivocally the largest thing I've ever eaten.'

'Amazingly, incredibly and extraordinarily large!' agreed the rest.

'Yes, yes,' said Himself, 'but what do you think of the flavour?'

'The flavour?' said Gabriel. 'Ah! The flavour! How can I describe it? Of course, I'm not an expert, but I'd say that it has an extremely large flavour.'

'Exactly!,' the others chimed in. 'It has an extraordinarily and uniquely large flavour. We couldn't have put it better ourselves!'

Himself turned to me, saying, 'You've been very quiet, Muriel. What have you got to say about My latest creation? Would you describe it as "large"?'

'Well, it is indubitably large but that's not the word I'd use to describe the flavour.'

'And what word would you use?'

'"Disgusting". It tastes stomach-churningly, gut-wrenchingly disgusting. What is it?'

'It's something you suggested yesterday. It's "sofa". And if you don't like it, you know where you can stick it!'

I took Him at His word. Which is how the 'sofa' came to be stuck in the corner of the room until someone could think of a use for it. I can't exactly remember who came up with the idea of a purpose for left-over 'sofa' but, typically, Himself claimed the credit, as He did for all good ideas. However, after it had stood in the corner for a couple of thousand years, somebody had the bright idea of using it as a place to lose things. For example, if one of us couldn't find our halo the others would say: 'I bet it's behind the "sofa".' Or 'Have you looked under the "sofa"?' Or, alternatively, 'I wouldn't be the slightest bit surprised if it hasn't fallen down the side of the "sofa".' So we'd go and look. And nine times out of ten we would discover the missing object behind, under or in the 'sofa'. Yes, the perfect function of a sofa was as a handy place to lose things.

One day, Gabriel came into the room, exhausted after his weight-training and, instead of hovering just above the ground, cooling himself off in the breeze from his wings, he casually slumped on to the 'sofa'. And, after a moment, he leapt into the air shouting, 'Eureka!'

We all turned to him in amazement and said, 'What does "eureka" mean?'

To which he replied, 'It means, "Bloody Norah, I've got a castor up my bum! And it isn't half painful".'

After that we steered well clear of the 'sofa' until, finally, we decided to throw it out. We put it in the back yard, but this time with the castors on the ground instead of sticking up in the air. And, looking at it, Gabriel said, 'I think I've found a better use for the "sofa".'

'Really?' we replied. 'What use?'

'Well, I've been looking at it very carefully. And judging from the size and shape and contours of it, it occurred to me that this "sofa" would make an absolutely perfect bonfire.'

So we set fire to it.

And when it had finished burning, Raphael picked up one of the embers saying, 'It looks good.' And he sniffed it, saying, 'By golly, it smells good.' And he licked it, saying, 'Mmmmm! It tastes good! It's really delicious! You know what?'

And I said, 'Don't tell me. The daft old so-and-so under-cooked it.'

The next thing I knew, the ground was shaking and there was the sound of thunder and through the thunder came the voice of Himself, saying:

'I heard that, Muriel!
And I've half a mind...'

Boasting again, I thought.

'And I also read that thought! Any more of your insolence and I will turn you into a toad.'

I was tired of His niggling, so I said, 'It can't be any worse than hanging around here all day, eating terrible food and entertaining myself by looking for things behind the "sofa". So go ahead, turn me into a toad.'

And Himself said, 'No. Not today.'

'Why not?'

'I don't feel like it.'

'You mean, You *can't* turn me into a toad.'

'Of course, I can. I am God Almighty, The Supreme and...'

'Omnipotent Being. Yes, I know all that. Go on, if You're so powerful, turn me into a toad.'

'Well, I would, but I've got a headache.'

And to demonstrate it, He ran His hand over His fevered knee and limped off to His bed.

Gabriel watched Him hobbling away and said, 'Verily, The Lord does move in mysterious ways.'

'Yea,' said the others. 'Verily, He does.'

I said nothing, but thought, how can I respect a Being who doesn't know His head from His knee? One day there are going to be some changes around here.

And that was The End of The Middle of The Beginning.

Chapter Four-ish

A Little Bit After The End of The Middle of The Beginning

ou might find it difficult to believe that the emnity between Himself and me started with such seeming trivialities as the names He gave me and the food He forced us to eat.[11]

But that just goes to show the pettiness of the so-called Supreme Being. There was absolutely no reason why He shouldn't have given me a suitably Biblical name. It was obvious that He took against me from the start just because I was different from the rest of the archangels. It was hardly my fault that while Gabriel, Raphael, Uriel and Zadkiel all had lustrous golden wings, mine were a rather curious sort of tartan, comprising vibrant green and a shade of orange that some might describe as 'electric' but which I always considered to be on the vulgar side of garish. I didn't choose the

---

11. *Publisher's note:* Yes, we do find it difficult to believe. In fact, we find it impossible. Just thought we'd mention that in case God is as petty as The Author claims and takes His revenge by doing something nasty, like turning us into one of the lower forms of pond life. Or, if He's feeling particularly vindictive, Belgians.

blasted things, He gave them to me and I can only conclude that in addition to being totally bald, He was also colour-blind.

Apart from these bloody great plaid things flapping round my back and making it incredibly difficult to sit down without creasing them – and sitting on your own wings really bring tears to your eyes, let me tell you; almost as bad as having a castor up your bum – I was different in other respects to the rest of the archangels.

For a start, they were all blond, while my hair was jet black, and this caused me no end of problems when I was a cherubim. The others teased me mercilessly, calling me names and doubting my paternity, which was ridiculous because as there was only Himself in the whole universe it rather narrowed down the list of possible candidates.

As I grew from cherubim to seraphim to archangelhood, I became increasingly self-conscious about my black hair and spent hours in the bathroom with bottles of peroxide trying to make myself look like the others. Even when I became a platinum blond, Gabriel never lost the opportunity to humiliate me by saying things like, 'Muriel, have you ever thought of painting your halo to match your wings? Oh, and by the way, your roots are showing.'

Himself was no better. As I grew up He never really forgave me for being taller than Him. In fact, all the arch-angels were taller than Him, standing as He did only five feet two inches even when wearing three pairs of His thickest socks. He couldn't bear the fact that the so-called Supreme Being had to look up to others but forgave Gabriel and the rest because they always stooped in His presence. However, being the tallest of all and refusing to stoop for anyone, I still towered above Him even when He was standing on the box He carried everywhere. This drove Him into a rage and eventually He took to wearing sandals with seven-inch plat-form heels. This made Him slightly happier until the day He tripped, fell off His shoes and hit the ground with a sickening crunch. Nothing was hurt but His pride, He didn't take kindly to having to crawl under the 'sofa' in order to retrieve His wig and, of course, He had to have someone to blame. Guess who? Most unfair. It was His own fault. If He's omniscient He should have known my foot was, by pure accident, sticking out in His path.

He is, as has often been pointed out, a jealous God and the way He got His revenge was by giving me stupid names.

As for the food: you must understand that in the early eons of Heaven there really wasn't anything to do, so all we had to look forward to were our meals. There was no entertainment, except for Raphael and his harp which he played every evening.

Each night, after yet another appalling meal, we'd all sit around this crummy shack, bored out of our minds, trying to while away the hours before bed.

Gabriel would polish his halo until he could see his own face in it and then he'd gaze lovingly at his reflection for hours, muttering, 'Who's a pretty angel, then?' Zadkiel would preen his wings incessantly, teasing them this way and that, saying, 'What do you think? Am I moulting or not? I'm almost certain that this feather is coming loose. I do hope it's not going to drop out. There's nothing worse than bedraggled plumage, makes one feel such a fright.'

Uriel would crawl around and under the 'sofa', hoping that something had been lost so he could shout, 'Look what I've just found! And you'll never guess where I found it!' To which the others would reply, 'Oh! Don't tell us! It wasn't under the "sofa", was it?'

I would just sit there, belching quietly, and wishing that the so-called Supreme Being had been omnipotent enough to create a cure for indigestion.

In the midst of this riveting hurly-burly Himself would boom: 'So! What shall we do this evening?'

We'd all say 'Ummm...er...That's a tough one. Let's have a long, hard think.'

Then He'd bellow, 'Hands up all those in favour of Raphael giving us a tune on his harp.'

All the others would shout: 'What a spiffing idea! Just what I fancy! Gosh You *are* clever! I wish I'd thought of that!'

And Raphael would go coy, 'Oh, you don't *really* want me to play my harp again.'

'Oh, yes, we do, Raphael! Honest!'

'Well, if you insist, but I'm terribly out of practice. I haven't even plucked a string since...oooh...it must have been last night. But here goes...'

He'd reach for his harp, run his fingers over the strings and say, 'What would you like me to play?'

To which Himself would reply, 'I don't know about anyone else, but what I'd really like to hear is something that praises My name.'

'Ooooh, yes!' they'd all chorus. 'What we'd really like to hear is something that praises Your name, too!'

And Raphael would say, 'What a truly extraordinary co-incidence! Because just this afternoon I wrote a little number that just happens to be called "Let's All Praise His Name" and it goes something like this...'

It always went exactly like...

Let's all praise His name!
Let's all praise His name!
Why don't we all join in and praise His name?
Yes, praise His name
Oh! praise His name
There really is nothing better in all of Heaven than
Praising His name!
So, let's all praise His name!

Then Raphael would insist that we all joined in the chorus:

Praise His name!
Praise His name!
Praise His name!
Praise His name!

Which was followed by the second verse:

Let's all praise His name!
Let's all praise His name!
Why don't we all join in and praise His name?
Yes, praise His name
Oh! praise His name
There really is nothing better in all of Heaven than
Praising His name!
So, let's all praise His name!

And when it was eventually finished, four hundred and

seventy verses later, Himself would say: 'Let's hear that one more time because I don't know what anyone else thinks but in My humble opinion – an opinion as humble as the Perfect and Supreme Being can manage – that was the very best song praising My name I've ever heard.'

And the others would all applaud and shout, 'Yes! Even better than the one last night, which we thought could not be improved. Raphael has done it again!'

And Raphael would blush and say, 'No, really, it wasn't *that* good. It still needs a lot of work. For instance, I don't think I quite praised Your name enough.'

'Perhaps you're right,' Himself would agree. 'There may be room for a touch more praise. But I don't want you overdoing it because all this praise, it might go to My knee! And I don't want to become a big-kneed God!'[12]

And so it went on, night after night, week after week, month after month, year after year, decade after decade, century after century, millennium after millennium. Perhaps it wouldn't have been so bad if (i) Raphael had known more than one tune and (ii) if the one tune he did know hadn't been so cretinously turgid.[13]

Each and every night, after we had praised His name, Himself would say, 'Well, it's been another Heavenly day and I'm ready for My bed, so I'm going up the little wooden hill.' And He'd go off to His room. Minutes later He'd come back, saying, 'Where's the staircase?'

And we'd remind Him that we lived in a bungalow.

Then the others would all agree that they'd had a really

---

12. When He referred to 'knee' He did, of course, mean 'head'. (See end of last chapter. Unless you already have. In which case, don't bother. Instead, why don't you indulge in a spot of wanton carnality?)

13. According to The Author, the tune bore an uncanny resemblance to 'Chirpy Chirpy Cheep Cheep'. Incidentally, this is the thirteenth footnote. It could be very very unlucky for one of you reading it at this moment. Especially if you are reading it on Friday the 13th. And more especially if, as you are reading it, you failed to notice the black cat which crossed your path a moment ago. And even more especially if you ignore the fact that you are just about to walk under a ladder. I have this message for you: Sorry you're not going to finish the book, but I'll tell you the rest of the story when I see you Downstairs!

divine evening and that they were ready to snuggle under the sheets. And Zadkiel would say, 'Yes, an early night for me because I think I'm coming down with a bad moult.' And we'd all go off to our rooms, get down on our knees beside our beds and say our prayers:

'God bless Gabriel, God bless Raphael, God bless Uriel, God Bless Zadkiel, God bless me and God bless Yourself.'

Then they'd all turn in and sleep the sleep of the just, not to say the sleep of the smugly self-righteous. All except me. I would sit up half of the night, staring out in the black, empty, featureless, infinite void of the universe and think, 'There *must* be more to eternal life than this! Somewhere there *has* to be something more interesting.'

But there wasn't.

One evening, after a peculiarly dreadful supper...another of His experiments; this time it was a barbecue. Terribly indigestible, especially the metal legs...Anyway, after it the others were all saying: 'What shall we do tonight?'

'Ummm, that's a tough one.'

'I know! Let's try to persuade Raphael to give us a tune on his harp!'

'Brilliant idea!'

I could stand it no longer. So I said, 'Do you know what I'd *really* like?'

'Yes, Muriel, what you'd *really* like is to join in singing "Let's All Praise His Name!".'

'No, I wouldn't. I'd like to do something else for a change.'

'Something else? Like what?'

'Well, I'd like to go out somewhere and get stoned.'

'You want to go out and get stoned? What a really wizard idea!'

And so we all went out and they stoned me.

The next morning, when I emerged rather later than usual, they asked, 'You're not looking too bright. Didn't you enjoy your night out?'

'Let's just say I've got a terrible headache and my mouth feels as though an ostrich has urinated into it.'

'So you don't like going out and getting stoned.'

'To be quite frank, it wasn't exactly what I had in mind.'

'So, what *did* you have in mind?'

'Well, somehow I thought I might drink something – something other than nectar – and it would make me feel happy and I'd laugh and joke and sing and dance and then stagger to my bed to fall happily into a dreamless sleep. Then I'd wake up in the morning and...'

'And?'

'Have a terrible headache and my mouth would feel like an ostrich had urinated into it.'

'What sort of drink,' they asked, 'would do all that?'

'I don't know, but I think He should invent one.'

'So,' said Gabriel, 'given that you are covered in black and blue bruises which, if I may say so, clash horribly with your tartan wings, and given that you have a terrible headache and that your mouth feels as though an ostrich – whatever *that* may be – has urinated in it, I suppose that you will never ever want to go out and get stoned again.'

'Not at all. I think I'll do the same thing tonight. After all, having large rocks slung at you is better than listening to Raphael playing the harp.'[14]

So once a week I'd go out with the boys and they'd sling rocks at me. It wasn't much, but it was better than nothing. The others really enjoyed it, especially Gabriel because it gave him good practice for being an avenging angel and built up his pectoral muscles at the same time. And I found that I was starting to enjoy the pain and had quite inadvertently invented masochism billions of years before my good friend Sacher de Masoch gave it his name, and that Gabriel had invented sadism billions of years before Sade gave it her name.[15]

That marked The End of The Middle Bit Before The Real Beginning Actually Began...

---

14. I really hate that instrument and have banned it from Hades. Above the front gate is a sign saying, 'Abandon harp all ye who enter here.'

15. When we pointed out that sadism was named after the Marquis de Sade who specialized in torture and not the pop star Sade, The Author responded: 'Have you heard her sing? She inflicts more pain and punishment than he ever did.'

Chapter...Um??[16]

The Start of The Last Bit Before The Real Beginning Actually Began

 remember waking up one Lawnmower with a particularly bad headache.[17] It was caused, I recall, by an unusually large rock thrown by Gabriel with unnecessary relish. So, in addition to my bruises, I was also uncomfortably sticky from the tomato sauce.[18]

As I lay in my bed I viewed the events of the coming day in Heaven. I would get up as usual. I would say my morning prayers – 'Thank You God for blessing Gabriel. Thank You God for blessing Raphael. Thank You God for blessing Uriel. Thank You God for blessing Zadkiel. Thank You God for blessing me. And most of all, thank You God for blessing Yourself' – as usual. I would have breakfast – ambrosia washed down with nectar – as usual.

After breakfast I would put on my clean white frock as usual. And I would go outside as usual. And within minutes my clean white frock would get grubby as usual. And I would

---

16. This is Chapter Five. In seeking to confuse, The Author has become confused.

go inside and wash it as usual. Everything would go on as usual. As usual. And as usual, I would be bored rigid. But, unusually, on this particular dark and dismal Lawnmower morning I had an idea.[19]

I leapt from my bed and went rushing into the kitchen where Himself was dishing up breakfast and the others were asking, 'What's for breakfast this morning, God?'

'Well,' He replied, 'I thought that you might like some ambrosia and nectar.'

'Ambrosia and nectar! How absolutely scrummy! You really do spoil us!'

I was bursting with excitement and shouted, 'Listen everyone, I've just had an idea!'

Everyone stopped in their tracks and Himself turned to me and said, 'An idea! You've just had an idea?'

'Yes, I've just had this really great idea!'

And Himself said, 'Well done, Muriel! I never knew you had it in you!'

And the others shouted, 'Yes, well done Muriel! We never knew you had it in you!'

And Himself gazed upon me and said, 'What exactly *is* an "idea"?'

'An "idea"? Well, how can I explain it in words that You'll

---

17. Lawnmower was the fifth day of the week. According to The Author, during the infancy of the universe everything was given an arbitrary name. If the name seemed to fit, it was kept, if not it was changed and the word given to something else. At that time, the days of the week were Courgette (Sunday), Dishwasher (Monday), Drain (Tuesday), Particle (Wednesday), Lawnmower (Thursday), Gastritis (Friday) and Wubblypoop (Saturday). Of these only Wubblypoop has been lost to linguistics although, according to The Author, it was used in the Atlantan tongue to describe the pus emanating from a large boil after it has been squeezed. As the continent of Atlantis reputedly sank beneath the ocean, there is no way of verifying this claim. Nor another of The Author's assertions that 'Tuesday' was originally the word for using a vacuum cleaner as an enema.

18. Tomato sauce: it seems that Gabriel used to smear rocks with this relish in the mistaken belief that he could eat them.

19. Every morning in Heaven was dark and dismal because Himself had not yet created the sun.

understand? Basically, an "idea" is an image of an external object formed by the mind, isn't it?'

'Of course it is,' He said, 'I knew that. I know everything, being as I am, omnisc..., omnish...omn...oh, what's that word again?'

'Omniscient. It means all-knowing.'

'Exactly, that's Me, omni-what'sname...all-knowing.'

'Excuse me,' said Gabriel, 'but I haven't quite grasped this "idea" thing.'

'Well,' I explained, 'an "idea" is a notion, a thought, an impression. It's any product of intellectual action or of memory and imagination. It's an abstraction, an archetype, a concept, a conjecture, a hypothesis, an inkling, a perception, a surmise, a theory, a vision. That's an "idea".'

And the others were thunderstruck and looked at me aghast until Gabriel said, 'Oh, so *that's* an "idea". Tell me, can you eat it?'

'No, you can't eat it, Gabriel.'

'Pity.'

'At least, I don't think you can.'

'Well, it's not much use to us, is it?'

And God said, 'What is this wonderful, marvellous, terrific, incredible, utterly brilliant "idea"?'

'Well,' I explained, 'it just came to me this morning. I suddenly thought that instead of doing what we usually do all day...'

'Yes?' said Himself.

'We should try doing...'

'Yes?'

'Something...'

'Something. Yes?'

'Well, something...*else*!'

'Something else?'

'Exactly!'

'Something else like what?'

'I don't know like what, my idea hasn't quite got that far. But, basically, I thought we should all do something else for a change.'

'But,' said Himself, 'there isn't anything else. There's only this.'

CHAPTER...UM??

'That's my point. Why can't You, with that infinite omnipotence of which You keep boasting, create something to do?'

'I see,' He said and fell silent.

After a few minutes I said, 'Of course, if You *can't* create something, You only have to say so. I mean, we won't think any the worse of You.'

Then He spake, and when He spake, it was like unto an earthquake that made all Heaven tremble and heave beneath our quivering feet and caused bits of plaster to fall from the ceiling.

'OF COURSE I CAN CREATE SOMETHING!' spake He. 'ANYTHING! I CAN CREATE THINGS THE LIKE OF WHICH YOU CAN'T EVEN IMAGINE. I AM THE LORD THY GOD! I AM THE ALMIGHTY! THE ULTIMATE AND SUPREME PERFECTION WHOSE PUISSANCE IS WITHOUT LIMIT!

THERE IS NOTHING, BUT NOTHING, I CANNOT CREATE!'

And when the trembling and heaving had subsided and after we'd dusted the plaster out of our hair, I said, 'So what's stopping You?'

'I just can't think *what* to create. I mean, it's all very well for you to say, "Go on, create something" but you're not so clever when it comes to suggesting what I might create, are you? So come on, Mr Smartie-Boots, you tell Me what to create. Where are your so-called "ideas" now?'

'We—ell...'

'Yes?'

'Well, just off the top of my head, why don't You try creating somewhere else?'

'What do you mean by "somewhere else"?'

'I mean, somewhere that isn't *here*. Somewhere we could go to for an evening, or could take a trip to on a Courgette afternoon, see the sights and maybe have a picnic.'[20]

20. For those of you who can't remember a simple fact from one page to another, 'Courgette' is Sunday. This is the twentieth footnote; it's a little-known fact that twenty is an *incredibly* unlucky number for some. Especially if your name happens to be Peter Chatto and you're reading this in bed while smoking a cigarette. See you soon, Pete!

'And where do you suggest I might put this "somewhere else"?'

'Well, anywhere in the tractless void of infinite space. After all, there's enough of it to choose from.' I pointed at random into the empty vastness and said, 'Why not put it there?'

He followed the direction of my finger, screwed up His eyes, gazed into the meaningless, measureless blankness and said, 'What, there?'

'Yes, that'll do.'

'No, not there. Too...well, meaningless. And also measureless. I have decided, in My infinite wisdom, that it should be a smidgin lower and slightly to the left.'

Typical!

But without more ado He rolled up His sleeves, straightened His halo, climbed on His box and from this exulted position He stared intently into the fathomless depths of space, concentrating all His mental and spiritual energy on one minuscule, measureless and, indeed, meaningless spot. Then, raising His hand, He pointed His finger and boomed:

'I AM THE LORD GOD ALMIGHTY, SUPREME AND OMNIPOTENT BEING, CREATOR OF HEAVEN AND... WELL, JUST HEAVEN SO FAR, BUT THAT'S BESIDE THE POINT...HEAR YE MY WORDS AND OBEY THIS, MY COMMAND:
LET THERE BE...UM..."SOMEWHERE ELSE"!'

No sooner had He uttered these words than, in a deafening crash of thunder, a searing lightning bolt scorched from Him, streaking headlong into the benighted pit of nothingness, speeding ever onwards and outwards until it became but a pinprick of light. And just as it was about to disappear, the void erupted into a holocaust of blazing light, a massive conflagration made even more awesome by its terrible silence.

Eventually, when the blaze diminished and the smoke cleared, we could just make something out, infinitesimal but perceptible and glowing faintly against the surrounding stygian gloom. Something that could only be described as 'something'. And this 'something' was His creation.

CHAPTER...UM??

We fell involuntarily to our knees, and then abased ourselves, face down, on the ground beneath His feet, quaking before the colossal magnificence of His power.

One by one we raised our fearful faces to gaze upon Him. He stood there, shimmering and golden, as a reverential silence reigned until Gabriel, his voice small and tremulous with wonder, whispered: 'And God said, "Let there be 'somewhere else'." And lo! there *was* "somewhere else"!'

And God Almighty looked down upon us and spake unto us, saying, 'Bloody Norah! It actually *worked*!'

Chapter Something Or Other[21]

The Start of The Last Bit Before The Real Beginning Actually Began...Later That Same Lawnmower...

allelujah! Hallelujah! Hallelujah! God has created "somewhere else"!' shouted Gabriel, Uriel and Zadkiel. 'Hallelujah! Hallelujah! Whatever that means.'

'I've just decided,' said Himself, 'that it means "Praise My Name".'

So Raphael grabbed his harp and started singing:

'Let's all hallelujah!
Let's all hallelujah!
Why don't we all join in and hallelujah?
Yes, hallelujah!
Oh! hallelujah!
There really is nothing better in all of Heaven than hallelujahing!
So let's all hallelujah!'

21. This is, of course, Chapter Six. Or is it Chapter Five?

CHAPTER SOMETHING OR OTHER

...until God told him to shut up because He had a splitting kneegraine, brought on by exerting His immense powers.[22] Then He turned to me and said, 'There you are, Muriel, you wanted Me to create "somewhere else" and I have. What have you to say to that?'

'Very good. I have to admit I'm impressed. But just one teensy point...'

'Yes?'

'How do we get there?'

'Pardon?'

'What is the point of having "somewhere else" to go, if we can't get there? How are we going to transport ourselves from here to "somewhere else"?'

'Um...er...yes, well, I thought we could perhaps...um ...fly there.'

'Fly there?' said Gabriel.

'Yes, fly there. Using your wings. Remember your wings? They're the large flappy things attached to your back.'

'But,' Gabriel protested, 'You can't seriously mean that we fly all the way to "somewhere else", it must be...oooh, a million, billion, trillion miles away. And we've never flown farther than the wall at the end of the yard.'

And Zadkiel chipped in, 'You don't really expect me to fly a squillion miles when my feathers might moult at any moment! It could be seriously dangerous, not to mention what a fright I'll look when I arrive!'

'Of course,' Raphael added, 'I wouldn't *mind* flying a quintillion miles through the uncharted infinity of space, without a map or even some directions scribbled on the back of an envelope, but I do think someone should stay behind here, just in case the milkman calls.'

'Don't be stupid,' said Himself. 'I haven't created a milkman yet. And even if I had, he wouldn't call until Wubblypoop morning and this is only Later That Same Lawnmower.'

'Well in that case,' said Raphael, 'I'll just stay here and practise my hallelujahs so that I can *really* praise Your name if...I mean, when You return.'

Finally we decided to put it to the vote. Those in favour of

22. A migraine of the knee.

flying – one. Those against – four. Abstentions – me. It was the one and only time I ever abstained from anything in my entire existence, but on this occasion I felt that while I didn't object to stretching my wings and certainly relished an adventure, I wasn't too confident about Himself's skills as a navigator. It's difficult to trust yourself to someone who lives in a one-storey house and still thinks He goes upstairs to bed every night.

'So,' Uriel asked, 'if we're not going to fly, how are we going to get from here to "somewhere else"?'

And He said, 'I don't know! I'm knackered from exerting My immense powers, why doesn't Muriel come up with one of his "ideas". What do you say, Mr Clever Clogs?'

I thought for a moment. 'What we need is a cart, and before You ask, I don't know exactly what a cart is but can't You create something that will carry the six of us in comfort from here to there, and even from hither to yon and back again? And when You've done that, perhaps You'd also like to knock up a couple of horses to draw the cart?'

'Horses?' He said, 'What are horses?'

'I'm not sure, but perhaps they could be large, strong four-legged animals with flowing manes and long swishy tails.'

'Oh, you mean toads. No, I don't want to be whisked from here to "somewhere else" by toads, thank you very much. I am, after all, God, and I do have a certain image to maintain. I like to think that I can create Myself something better than a two toadpower cart.'

So saying, He drew Himself up to His full five feet two inches, pulled in His stomach, puffed out His chest, closed His eyes in concentration and clicked His fingers.

A CLAP! of thunder,
a FLASH! of lightning,
a PUFF! of smoke

and lo! there was a thingy. Not just any thingy but a burning, flame-covered thingy.

And we all said, 'Lo! He's done it again! Yea, this time He's created a burning, flame-covered thingy! Tell us, O Lord, what is it that You have created just by clicking Your fingers?'

'That is a chariot. Which is like a cart but posher, having, as it does, three extra letters in its name, not to mention independent suspension on both wheels. Is it not finger-clicking good? And no, Gabriel, you can't eat it.'

'Pity,' said Gabriel hungrily as the flames roared higher around it, 'because it's done to a turn.'

'As you can see,' continued Himself, 'this is not just any old chariot, but My extra-special Chariot of Fire, complete with optional extras like rear parking light and built-in cigar lighter. But without old-fashioned toadpower. Now hop aboard and we'll take a look at "somewhere else".'

Thus did we voyage through the immense black bleakness of space aboard His Chariot of Fire, whose flames illumined the dreadful darkness, casting light all around and causing us to sweat like pigs. In the twinkling of a...well, a twinkle ...it had transported us across the measureless miles and landed us on "somewhere else".

As we surveyed His creation, Himself said, 'So, Muriel, what do you think of "somewhere else"? Is it not good?'

And I gazed upon it, upon the shack painted ditchwater brown and sludge green, upon the plumbing which left a lot to be desired, like pipes, running water and a toilet seat and replied, 'Unless my eyes deceive, it is exactly the same as Heaven.'

'So?'

'So, call me naive if you will, but somehow I thought it would be different.'

'No, I will not call you Naive as you already have a perfectly good name. And what do you mean by different? When you asked Me to create "somewhere else" you didn't mention anything about it being different.'

'Swipe me,' I thought to myself, 'The Supreme Being has the I.Q. of a radish.'

And He said, 'I read that thought, Muriel! And I take it as a compliment, seeing as I will one day create an intelligence that is almost equal to Mine and which will run the universe while I am taking a well-earned rest. That superbrain will be

SATAN

called a "radish". Now, what's all this "different" business?'[23]

'How shall I put this?' I said, 'Look, it never occurred to me that The Supreme Being, whose intelligence is infinite and even greater than a radish's will be, would make "somewhere else" exactly the same as the place we were getting away from. So exactly and precisely the same that "somewhere else" doesn't have a toilet seat either.'

'Really,' He said, 'I go to all the bother and effort of creating a whole new place in the infinite universe, not to mention providing first-class, fire-driven transport and remembering to pack a hamper of nectar and ambrosia in case we feel peckish and still he complains! Some archangels are never satisfied!'

'Well,' said Gabriel, 'I really like it.'

'So do I,' agreed Raphael.

'Me too,' said Uriel.

'I think it's absolutely gorgeous,' said Zadkiel, 'it reminds me of home.'

'So there, Mr Spoilsport!', said Himself.

Patiently I explained that the whole purpose of creating somewhere else was to have a place we could visit that wasn't anything like Heaven, somewhere completely and utterly different.

So God said, 'All right! All right! I'll make it different. Anything to stop you complaining.' And He clicked his fingers.

A CLAP! of thunder

A FLASH! of lightning

And a PUFF! of smoke

23. Eventually, He did create the radish and it did have an intelligence vastly superior to that of any other life-form in the universe, except His. But the radish was so mind-bogglingly intelligent that when it thought about how intelligent it was, its mind literally boggled at the sheer effort. Having reduced itself to an I.Q. of zero, it settled contentedly for being a salad vegetable which gets its revenge for being eaten by causing acute indigestion and making people belch embarrassingly at exactly the wrong moment.

CHAPTER SOMETHING OR OTHER

'And lo!,' He said, 'it has come to pass! The "somewhere else" is different!'

And the others all jumped up and down and chanted, 'Lo! He's done it yet again! What a blinder! It is completely different! Yea, verily, now we have a shack painted dingy grey and muddy beige.'

And He spake, saying, 'Nay, verily, it is not dingy grey and muddy beige, it is Candyfloss Pink and Mediterranean Blue.'

To which the others replied, 'Oh, sorry, our mistake!'

But I said, 'If You think those colours are Candyfloss Pink and Mediterranean Blue, You need Your eyes tested!'

'There is nothing wrong with My eyes.'

'Is that so? Then why, despite Your infinite wisdom – about which we hear so much – do You seem to have difficulty distinguishing one shade from another?'

'I do not have difficulty,' He snapped, 'I am infallible. And omnipotent. And that other word meaning "all-knowing" which seems to have slipped My mind for the moment. You're just saying that because you're envious of My immense powers. You, Muriel, are purple with envy.'

'You mean green with envy.'

'DON'T ARGUE!'

'I'm not arguing, I'm simply pointing out an error of fact. There's no need to get so ratty just because You won't admit You're colour-blind.'

'I AM NOT COLOUR-BLIND!'

'Excuse me, but You are.'

'IF YOU ARGUE WITH ME ONCE MORE, I'LL TURN YOU INTO A TOAD!'

'Well, please Yourself but it doesn't seem a very adult way of ending a discussion.'

'RIGHT! THAT'S IT! YOU'VE ASKED FOR IT! JUST ONE CLICK OF MY FINGERS AND...'

And nothing.

'Are You,' I asked, 'having trouble getting Your immense powers to work?'

'NO, I'M NOT. IF YOU MUST KNOW, I'M JUST HAVING TROUBLE CLICKING MY FINGERS.'

'In that case,' said Gabriel, ever-helpful, 'lick Your thumb and forefinger. That's right. Now try again.'

SATAN

'AS I WAS SAYING, IT TAKES JUST ONE CLICK OF
MY FINGERS AND...

CLAP!
FLASH!
PUFF!

'So there! And what have you got to say to that, Mr Toad?'
'Um...Neeeeeeeeigh!'

Chapter Seven
or Maybe Eight[24]

*The Start of The Last Bit
Before The Etc., Etc.*

*A Teensy Bit Later That
Same Lawnmower…*

ll things considered, being a toad wasn't so
bad. Obviously, suddenly having four legs
took some getting used to, especially deciding which should be on the ground and
which should be off the ground at any one
time. After rather a lot of falling over I finally got the hang of
having a leg at each corner which is rather like being an
occasional table. In my time, of course, I have been an occasional table. I've also been an occasional wardrobe and,
when it has suited my evil purpose a very, very occasional
three-piece suite in uncut moquette. (When you do as much
seducing as I, it comes in handy being able to change your
form at will. Saves you a lot of unpleasantness from cuckolded
husbands. Or, indeed, wives, depending upon the gender of
the lucky person I happen to be seducing. However, you have
to be quick-witted. I recall one occasion when an outraged
husband burst in just as I had enjoyed carnal knowledge of
his spouse. In a flash I changed form. But I think he was

24. This is definitely, indubitably and unarguably Chapter Seven. We think.

suspicious about finding his wife in bed with a potting shed. Not that he could do much about it. His lawyer advised him he was unlikely to get a divorce on the grounds of her adultery with a semi-permanent garden structure, even given that they lived on the twenty-seventh floor of a highrise block of flats. And further advised him to seek psychiatric help. But not until he'd presented a hefty bill for his services.)

There I go, digressing again. Where was I? Ah, yes, being a toad. Not a bad life. I liked having the flowing mane and really loved the swishy tail. In fact, I loved it so much that I later adopted a tail of my own which, despite what you hear, I don't wear all the time but keep for special occasions. You should see me on Gala Orgy Nights in Hades, dressed up to the nines in my top hat, white tie and tail.[25]

As you've almost certainly guessed, unless you're particularly dense, which, after my experience of tricking and deceiving countless generations of you gullible fools, wouldn't surprise me, The Great Fraud got it wrong again. What He thought was a toad was, of course, a horse and, as a horse, I was quite content. Not to say, really very happy.

You see, horses have certain things that archangels don't. Apart from the two extra legs, the flowing mane and the swishy tail, I very soon became aware that I now possessed something else. And a very large something else at that. How shall I put this? Well, you never hear it said of any man that he's hung like a toad, do you? And you certainly don't hear it of archangels who, despite certain attributes like halos and enormous wings, are notably deficient in the groin area.

---

25. Every night is Orgy Night in Hades but once in a while we have a Gala Orgy at which the guests must perform seven different sexual acts with an animal, vegetable or mineral with which they've never previously had an intimate relationship. Sometimes they have to perform one sexual act with seven different animals, vegetables or minerals; I leave the details to the creature who arranges the evening, Bogsnatch. I call him my orgyniser. Not a very good joke but it amuses him. Mind you, most things amuse him, including wrenching the wings off rabbits. You didn't know rabbits had wings did you? And of course they don't, until Bogsnatch has hammered them into their backs with six-inch nails. A rather simple-minded hobby but it keeps him entertained.

To put it bluntly, they have nothing whatsoever there. Gabriel, for example, had even less between his legs than he had between his ears, which is saying something considering he was not quite as intelligent as your average radish, even after its mind had so spectacularly boggled.

You may, therefore, be able to imagine my surprise when it became apparent to me that I was now the possessor of an added attribute. And you may possibly be able to imagine my delight when I discovered that this attribute could do something considerably more interesting and enjoyable than just making water.[26]

I hadn't been a horse more than a few minutes when I started to experience what can best be described as 'stirrings'. (Actually, they can best be described as something quite different, but the publishers, miserable maggots that they are, censored my manuscript. May they rot in Hull.)[27]

These delicious 'stirrings' were as nothing I'd ever experienced before. Mind you, I'd hardly experienced *anything* before in the way of sensual delights, least of all of the gastronomic variety. My only physical pleasure had come from a comfy but chaste bed and being on the receiving end of large and jagged rocks. I realize the latter is not to everyone's taste, but then most of you don't know what you're missing – if you did you wouldn't be quite so squeamish about such delectably diverting activities as sucking the living brains out of nuns. But that's neither here nor there. It's somewhere else entirely, usually a convent in the dead of night.

---

26. *Publisher's note:* this raises an interesting theological and, indeed, biological question: if archangels do not possess the organ in question, how do they go to the toilet? The Author's answer is, 'They don't, archangels have no bodily functions at all.' In which case, we asked, why does he claim to have been so critical of the alleged toilet facilities offered in Heaven? To which he replied, 'I lied.'

27. *Miserable Maggots' note:* for any readers who are not conversant with the geography of The British Isles, Hull is a city on the east coast of England, standing on the estuary of the River Humber. It was once the centre of a thriving fishing industry but is now more noted as a major container port. We would like to make it clear that in our opinion this bustling little metropolis bears absolutely no relation to Hell, except, of course, that it too is a God-forsaken place.

SATAN

All-in-all, I rated these unexpected 'stirrings' as being vastly superior to both a comfy bed and a jagged rock. However, in my utter innocence, I was puzzled. I didn't understand the purpose of said 'stirrings'. I was becoming increasingly aware of a growing presence in my loin but perplexed as to what to do about it. And, indeed, with it.

At first I thought it might be some form of extra limb, a fifth leg perhaps, but rejected the notion when I realized that long though it was, it didn't quite reach the ground. Next I wondered if it served a similar purpose to my swishy tail as a device for deterring flies and pests. I swished it vigorously once or twice, so vigorously that it smacked sharply against my offside back leg, causing considerable pain and rather less pleasure than I'd hoped. I realized it would have been useless as a fly-whisk unless one managed an incredible, almost impossible, degree of accuracy.

Once I'd regained my breath and my eyes had stopped smarting, I noticed that this experiment resulted in my 'stirrings' becoming diminished. Indeed, they had almost disappeared, which was extremely disappointing because I was just beginning to thoroughly enjoy them.

But, try as I might, I could not regain them and in their absence I decided to put all four of my legs to the test with a short canter. Having managed to reach a respectable speed after only tripping twice when my nearside back became entangled with my offside front, and having practised a bit of whinnying and nostril-flaring, I looked around for further entertainment, preferably of the 'stirrings' variety. Finding none, I settled for a session of mane-tossing and tried pricking up my ears.

No sooner had I pricked up my ears (which should not, in any way, be construed as discovering a use for my 'stirrings') than I heard a sound, a sound like muffled thunder, as though Himself was speaking to me from a very great distance.

Looking around I discovered the source of the noise — thudding hooves. I was not alone. Rushing towards me was another four-legged creature, complete with flowing mane and swishing tail. It approached at a gallop, without once mistaking its back legs for its front, slowed to a trot and then reared on its hind legs.[28]

CHAPTER SEVEN OR MAYBE EIGHT

It opened its mouth and said, 'Cesspit!'

'Pardon?' said I.

'Cesspit, that's my name.'

'Cesspit', I said. 'What a lovely name!'

'Thank you,' it said. 'What's yours?'

'Um...well, actually, it's Muriel. But I'm thinking of changing it.'

'Yes,' said Cesspit, 'you should. Around here "Muriel" means "vile tapeworm that gnaws into the gut, has lamentable table manners and never ever says 'Pardon' after it breaks wind".'

'What do you suggest I change it to?'

'Well, "Pustule" is very popular at the moment, but looking at you I would suggest "Dobbin" which means "beautifully formed but having a coat that is a rather curious sort of tartan, comprising vibrant green and a shade of orange that some might describe as 'electric' but which I consider to be on the vulgar side of garish".'

'Yes,' I said, 'horrible isn't it?'

'Oh, I don't know. On you it looks good. You've got the fetlocks to carry it off.'

'Do you really think so?'

'Certainly.'

'Thank you.'

'You're welcome. Now, do you want to screw yourself brainless or what?'

'I beg your pardon?'

'I said, "Do you want to..."'

'Yes, I know what you said, but what does it mean?'

'What does it mean? Where have you been?'

28. When asked how it was possible for another creature to exist before God has created it, The Author replied, 'I was in the space–time continuum where anything and everything is possible. It's a strange and mysterious plane of being where the impossible happens so regularly that it becomes commonplace and miraculous phenomena are hardly worth mentioning. The space–time continuum is so impossibly amazing that even the trains arrive according to schedule, you can find a policeman when you need one and the taxi drivers actually know where they are going. Although, of course, they're still surly and rude. Even where the impossible is possible, some things, like polite and caring cab drivers, are just *too* impossible.'

'Well, actually, I've been in Heaven.'

'In Heaven! Pull the other one. No, don't bother, I'll pull your other one.'

Which is exactly what Cesspit did and immediately I began to feel my 'stirrings' again.

'Well, at least you know what *that* is for.'

'Er...well...actually I don't.'

And so Cesspit told me. Told me about males, which, apparently is what I was, and females,which is what she was. And she told me precisely and in graphic anatomical detail what males do to females when they both have 'stirrings'. As she told me all this I became greatly 'stirred'. Seeing how tremendously and obviously 'stirred' I was she said, 'So, do you want to screw yourself brainless?'

'Yes, please, if that's all right with you.'

She sighed resignedly, 'Oh all right, you've talked me into it, you silver-tongued smoothie.'

Then she winked, licked her lips and, flicking her tail in the most delightfully lascivious manner, turned around to display her pert, round perfectly-formed hocks, saying, 'Come and get it, big boy!'

I needed no second bidding. With one bound I was behind her, ears pricked, nostrils flaring. I threw back my head, tossed my mane, reared up on to my back legs, and with a cry of joy, thrust my newly-found tumescence towards her and...

CLAP!
FLASH!
PUFF!

Chapter...Um...The One After Last[29]

Enormous Breasts

CLAP!

    FLASH!

       PUFF!

ne second I was about to savour my first taste of erotic delight, the next I found myself back at the dingy shack, peering into the gloom, standing in front of Himself and the others, lounging on the ground.

'Welcome back, Muriel! Being a merciful God, I have decided to forgive you and so I've returned you to the infinite joys of Heaven. I trust your short but miserable existence as a toad has taught you the error of your ways and that in future we'll have no more of your nonsense. Now, sit down, have an ambrosia sandwich and we'll say no more about it.'

'Yes,' carolled the others, 'have an ambrosia sandwich, which He has cleverly invented by putting ambrosia between two bits of sliced manure! Verily, this sandwich is the most blissful of all the myriad and wondrous things in God's creation!'

'You wouldn't say that if you'd ever experienced a "stirring".'

'Pardon?'

---

29. We are almost certain this is Chapter Eight. But who cares?

'Nothing. Now, if you don't mind, I'll forgo the sandwich, I just want to pop inside to check something.'

I went indoors to my bedroom. I locked the door behind me, closed the curtains and, hidden from prying eyes, I lifted up my frock, pulled down my scanty French directoire knickers and looked between my legs to find...nothing.

I was once again what I had always been, a genderless archangel. An archangel robbed of the source of the most exquisite pleasure I had ever experienced. And, worse still, robbed of my ultimate sensual experience.

I wept bitter tears of frustration.

It was so unfair! All I had needed were another couple of minutes. Just two more minutes of lunging towards those pert little hocks and my pleasure would have been consummated. I had been trembling on the very brink of physical ecstasy, hovering tantalizingly close to the eruption of bodily desire and in an instant my joy had been snatched from me. At that very instant He had plucked me from the erotic brink; with one click of His fingers He had cheated me of my pleasure.

He had timed it to perfection. An instant later and bliss would have been mine. And I knew that the old bastard knew. He knew exactly what He was doing, exactly what He was denying me. Even then, as I wept in frustrated rage, He was sitting outside, munching His sandwich and laughing hysterically to Himself.

I would never forgive Him. I vowed there and then to get my revenge, I didn't care how long I waited, I would have my retribution, even if it took me a hundred thousand million years.

In fact it took me 99,999,999,999 years, seven months and six days. And the reason it took so long was The Really Triff And Absolutely Brill Plan...

CHAPTER...UM...THE ONE AFTER LAST

Meanwhile, Back in The Space–Time Continuum . . .

...a horse called Cesspit is saying, 'Come and get it, big boy!'

CLAP!

FLASH!

PUFF!

'Pardon? Where's he gone? Buggered off without so much as a goodbye! Typical! Bloody men, get you all worked up and then...nothing! Who needs them? Anyway, I didn't really fancy him, especially not in that ridiculous tartan coat. He's no great loss, for all his fine talk about his "stirrings", that stallion was hung just like a man, poor sod'.

At which point she was struck in the rear by a hurtling express train that was precisely 1.8 seconds behind schedule.

As a result of the impact the train was completely wrecked and Cesspit experienced an orgasm so gut-churningly intense that her brain imploded and she spent the rest of her life believing she was a toad. The rest of her life was, sadly, brief. She drowned when trying to hop from the edge of a pond on to a water-lily which was ill-equipped to take the weight of a lust-crazed horse.

At exactly the same instant, three and three-quarter miles away, a taxi driver was just abusing a passenger for the meanness of his tip when he had a mystic revelation. A vision came to him and revealed one of the great mysteries of the universe – he discovered where flies go in winter. As a result he drove his cab there, taking the long route via the airport and light industrial estate. After three frustrating weeks lost

61

in a contra-flow gyratory system, he gave up in disgust and turned down a dirty alley.

Why a large bearded woman should linger around a contra-flow gyratory system, waiting to approach taxi drivers and hiss out of the side of her mouth, 'Pssst! Wanna buy a dirty alley', is an unfathomable enigma.

But anything is possible in the space—time continuum.[30]

30. The more observant among you may have noticed that, despite the title of this chapter, there has not been one single reference to enormous breasts. I was going to call the chapter 'The Start of The End Bit Before The Real Beginning Actually Began...A Teensy-Weensy Bit Later That Same Lawnmower...' But somehow 'Enormous Breasts' seemed more eye-catching.

Chapter Nine[31]

The Really Triff And Absolutely Brill Plan

ursing my grudge in my heart, I determined not to give any sign of grievance. I readjusted my clothing over my nonexistent groin, wiped the salt tears from my eyes and returned outside.

'Hello, Muriel,' said Gabriel, 'did you find what you were looking for?'

'No.'

'I'll bet it's behind the "sofa".'

'I doubt it.'

'Let me go and have a look,' cried Uriel, 'I *love* looking under the "sofa"!'

'Don't bother. Actually, I'm quite peckish, are there any of those ambrosia sandwiches left?'

'No, we've eaten them all.'

'Well, thank you, thanks so very much.'

'No thanks needed, it was our pleasure!'

Himself, who'd been taking a nap in the afternoon gloom, abruptly woke up and declared, 'I've been thinking!'

31. Amazingly, this really *is* Chapter Nine. Honest.

'Hallelujah! God's been thinking! Tell us, O Lord, what have You been thinking?'

'One of the things I've been thinking is how incredible it is being Me! I can think even when I'm taking a nap! Is there no end to My genius?'

The others agreed that there wasn't.

'Just as I suspected. Anyway, apart from thinking how amazing it is that I'm thinking while taking a nap, I've also been thinking that I really quite enjoy this creating things lark, even though it is tiring and liable to give Me a headache, and I'd like to do more of it. So I've worked out this Really Triff And Absolutely Brill Plan.'

The others all clapped their hands and chortled, 'Oh, goody, goody! A Really Triff And Absolutely Brill Plan is just what we were hoping You'd work out! So, don't keep us in suspense any longer, what *is* this Really Triff And Etc., Etc?'

'Well, I'm so pleased with the way that "somewhere else" has turned out that I have decided, in My infinite wisdom, about which I may have spoken once or twice before, that I'm going to create more "somewhere elses". What do you think of that?'

'We think that truly this is Really The Triff-est And Absolutely Brill-est Plan of the type that only You, in Your infinite wisdom of which You may have spoken once or twice and maybe even thrice before, could come up with!'

He proceeded to detail The Plan.

'I have decided that there will be lots and lots of "somewhere elses", scattered throughout the firmament. And each will be a different "somewhere else" from the other. Some, for example, will be like as unto huge lumps of rock of the sort that you fling at Muriel but much, much bigger. Others will be enormous balls of seething gases. Some will be tiny and dainty, giving off pretty little glows of light that will twinkle and sparkle in the firmament and yet others will be truly massive and colossal and composed entirely of green cheese.'

The others all clapped their hands, jumped up and down and trilled, 'By golly, He's done it yet again! Blimey O'Reilly, He really is the sort of God you can look up to, even if He is definitely on the short side for a Supreme Being!'

And Gabriel added, 'This green cheese stuff, can you eat it?'

CHAPTER NINE

And God said, 'I don't know because I haven't created it yet. But even if you can, I don't want you gobbling up My beautiful "somewhere elses" as soon as I have created them.'

And He turned to me and said, 'Well, Muriel, what do you think of My Really Triff And Absolutely Brill Plan?'

'It sounds like a lot of hard work to me.'

'It will be hard work, Muriel, because all of you will help Me in this great endeavour. I will do all the creative work, like thinking up the ideas and sketching the designs for the "somewhere elses" and you will do all the heavy manual labour like shifting them around the firmament. And all this arduous toil will keep you so busy that you, Mr Misery Guts, won't have time to moan and whine and bitch and generally stir up trouble.

'My Really Brill And Absolutely Triff Plan will occupy us all, and especially *you*, for the next 99,999,999,999 years, seven months and six days, give or take a day. Yea, verily it can be said that God makes work for idle hands!'

And I contemplated the 99,999,999,999 years, seven months and six-ish joyless days of menial labour that lay ahead, days without 'stirrings', and said, 'I don't suppose You'd consider turning me back into a toad?'

'No!'

Chapter Ten

The Next 99,999,999,999 Years, Six Months And Twenty-Nine Days...

The next 99,999,999,999 years, six months and twenty-nine days seemed like an eternity. And, of course, they would be an eternity to the likes of you because you have a brief life-span which I, with my many guiles and subterfuges, attempt to make all the briefer in order to speed you to the bosom, not to mention the groin, of my family in Hades. But when you are infinite, millennia usually pass in the blinking of an eye.[32]

These millennia did not. The time dragged. For each of those 36,500,000,000,819 days we worked from dawn to dusk.

---

32. I'd just like to say how much I appreciate the help that many of you – particularly smokers, drinkers and drug addicts – give me in this task. It makes my job so much easier. And before those of you who have given up these delicious but deadly habits get too smug, allow me to remind you that the road to Hell is paved with good intentions. In fact, you might as well surrender to your vices because I'm going to get you one way or the other.

Publishers' note: The road to Hell should not be confused with the road to Hull, the A1, which, due to local government cutbacks, isn't paved at all.

CHAPTER TEN

No, that's not quite accurate; for 36,500,000,000,818 of them we worked from dawn to dusk. But on the first of them we worked from dusk to dusk as Himself had not yet created the seething mass of gases that was our sun.

On that very first morning we awoke to discover Himself was already up. In fact, He was about seven feet up, hovering cross-legged above the kitchen table, His eyes tightly closed, chanting to Himself, 'I am the champion! I am the champion! I am the champion!' Eventually He became aware of our presence and, blushing slightly, He explained, 'I'm just getting Myself psyched-up for the enormous task that lies before Me.'

'I didn't realize,' I said, 'that making breakfast was so taxing of Your omnipotence.'

'I shall ignore that facetious remark, except to say that in future I shall not be making breakfast. It is, I feel, a task too humble for The Supreme Being who has better things to do with His time like creating galaxies, solar systems, planets, stars and other celestial sundries. From now on you will each take turns to make the meals while I devote My energy to conceiving the multitudinous miracles that constitute My Really Triff And Absolutely Brill Plan.

'So, for the next thirty-six thousand, five hundred million eight hundred and eighteen days you Gabriel and you Raphael and Uriel and Zadkiel will be on brekky duty.'

'Yes, Lord,' they said obediently. 'But what about Muriel? What will he do for the next thirty-six thousand, five hundred million, eight hundred and eighteen days?'

'I have a very special and important task for Muriel, a task that, in My Infinite Wisdom, which I may have mentioned now and again, I have devised especially for him. Every day for the next thirty-six thousand, five hundred million, eight hundred and eighteen days Muriel will do the washing up. Perhaps that will teach him not to make Smart Alec remarks.'

And so it came to pass that for the next thirty-six thousand, five hundred million, eight hundred and eighteen days I did the washing up every morning. But what no one realized in all that time is that I washed their plates, cups, knives, forks and spoons by spitting on them and wiping them with a pair of my old knickers. Not a particularly evil deed compared

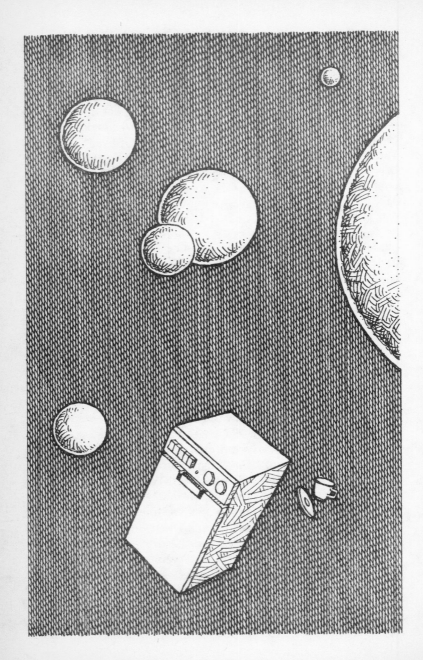

with the depths of depraved wickedness I was to plumb later, but at the time it was the naughtiest thing any archangel had ever done.

After breakfast and having finished the washing up on that very first morning, Himself gathered us around Him and spake, saying, 'This is the first morning of My Really Triff And Absolutely Brill Plan and I intend to start as I will continue, by creating something. Something that will amaze and astound you. And, as this is the start of our great enterprise together, I will allow you to choose what I will create. Any suggestions?'

'Well,' I said, 'what about creating an automatic dish-washer?'

'Shut up, Muriel, unless you want to be scrubbing the kitchen floor every evening for the next thirty-six thousand, five hundred million, eight hundred and eighteen days. Now, let's have some sensible suggestions. Gabriel?'

And Gabriel thought hard for several moments and said, 'Well, Lord, You remember how You created "somewhere else"?'

'Indeed I do.'

'How about creating another "somewhere else"?'

'Yes, that's a really topping idea,' the others chimed. 'Why not create another "somewhere else" and make it exactly like the "somewhere else" You've already created?'

'I was hoping,' said Himself, 'for something a trifle more challenging. I do so hate to repeat Myself.'

'In that case,' said Gabriel, 'maybe this new "somewhere else" could be much, much bigger.'

'Or much, much smaller,' said Raphael.

'Or maybe a bit squarer,' said Uriel.

'Or,' said Zadkiel, 'perhaps it could be slightly...um... furrier.'

'Furrier?'

'Yes. Furrier. Or even...er...wobblier. And when I say "wobblier", perhaps I mean it could be a bit more squiggly in a droopy sort of way. Or something.'

'Thank you, Zadkiel, for those invaluable suggestions. I must remember to make a careful note of them and throw it away. In the meantime, I shall ignore all your suggestions and create something of My own. And what I'm going to create are…mountains.'

'Ooh, goody goody gumdrops! God is going to create mountains! Whatever they may be.'

'Whatever they are, Lord,' said Gabriel, 'could You make them edible?'

But Himself was not listening, He had screwed up His eyes in intense concentration, raised His hand and, after a sharp intake of breath, He intoned:

'LET THERE BE MOUNTAINS!'

And He clicked His fingers…

CLAP!
FLASH!
PUFF!

When the smoke had cleared and our eyes had recovered from the dazzling light, we blinked in amazement at the sight which presented itself.

'By jingo!' we all shouted, 'He's only gone and done it again! Blow me, no sooner did The Lord say, "Let there be mountains", than there *were* mountains!'

'Verily,' quoth Gabriel, 'look at the unimaginable height of them!'

'Yea,' quoth Raphael, 'look at the awesome width of them!'

'Yea and verily!' quoth Uriel, 'look at the fearsome graniteness of them!'

'Yea, verily and lo!' quoth Zadkiel, 'look at the pretty water gushing out of the top of them!'

'Pardon?,' quoth Himself.

And Gabriel quoth back, 'Well, I quothed: "Verily, look at the unimaginable height of them!" Then Raphael quothed, "Yea! Look at the awesome…" '

'Forget all that. What was it that Zadkiel was just quothing?'

'All I quothed was, "Look at the pretty water gushing out of the top of them".'

And Himself looked and saw. 'I said "Let there be mountains." NOT fountains! What's the point of being omnipotent if I can't give the simplest order without something going wrong?'

And the others tried to placate Him, saying, 'Mountains, fountains, what's the difference?'

'The difference, dummies, is that I can't have a huge range of fountains spewing billions of gallons of water all over the place. Think of the mess it will make of My nice clean brand-new planets. It'll make them soggy. And there's nothing, but nothing, worse than a soggy planet.'

That's all He knew. But, of course, He'd never been rudely interrupted in the middle of a rattling good 'stirring'. I didn't actually point that out to Him. Instead, I asked, 'So, what are You going to do about these five-mile high fountains, which even now are pouring water at an alarming rate all over Heaven?'

'Um...well...I suppose I'll just have to uncreate them.'

'And how will You do that?'

'By reversing the whole process. Now stand back and give Me room to think.'

He unscrewed His eyes, lowered His hand and, after a sharp exhalation of breath, He outtoned:

'!SNIATNUOM EB EREHT TEL'

And He unclicked His fingers...

!FFUP

!HSALF

!PALC

And we witnessed it and cried: 'Crikey! He's only gone and undone it! Well, I'll be hornswoggled! No sooner did The Lord say, "!sniatnuom eb ereht teL", than there *were* no fountains!'

And Himself said, 'You ain't seen nothin' yet.' And He raised His hand yet again and screwed up His eyes and commanded:

'LET THERE BE MOUNTAINS!

That's mountains with an "m"! As in "m" for…um…'

'As in "m" for manure?', I suggested, helpfully.

'No! As in "m" for mnemonic!'

And with that the old show-off clicked His fingers…

CLAP!

FLASH!

PUFF!

And we witnessed it and cried, 'Stone the crows! He's done it one more time! No sooner did The Lord say, "Let there be mountains with an 'm', as in 'm' for mnemonic," than there *were* mountains!'

Himself did not yet unscrew His eyes. Instead, He said, 'You're quite sure they are mountains, with an "m" for mnemonic, and not fountains with an "f" for…well, for fotograph?'

'No,' we assured Him, 'they are definitely *not* fountains because there is no pretty water gushing out of the top of them.'

'Well, thank Me for that,' He said.

'Excuse me for saying this,' said I. 'Not that I know anything about mountains, but somehow I expected them to be bigger.'

'Bigger?' He said, slowly opening His eyes.

'Yes. Bigger; taller, wider and more sort of, well, mountain-ous.'

He looked at them, all five inches of them, and said, 'Yes, I suppose they could be somewhat bigger.'

'And pardon me if I'm wrong,' I continued, 'but I also had the impression that they might be rockier.'

'Rockier?'

'Yes. Somehow I thought they'd be made of rock and granite and maybe marble instead of, well, crumbly bits of earth.'

He looked at them again and said, 'Yes, I suppose *some* people might expect them to be a touch rockier. But what you don't understand, Muriel, is that I have wrought a miracle. I, in My omnipotence, have done what no other being could do, I have made molehills out of mountains. Is not My power awesome and wondrous in the extreme?'

And the others all hymned, 'Yea, verily, Your power *is* awesome and wondrous in the extreme. And we really, truly like Your mountains, even though they tend towards the small and crumbly.'

'All right, all right,' He said, 'You don't have to go on about their smallness and crumbliness. To prove that I am truly and unquestionably omnipotent, I will now turn these admittedly not very large or particularly craggy mountains into something that will take your breath away.'

So saying, He went through His familiar little ritual yet again intoning:

'LET THERE BE MOUNTAINS. AND LET THEM BE HUGE, MASSIVE AND BLOODY GI-NORMOUS!'

CLAP!

FLASH!

PUFF!

'Cor! Is there no end to His true and unquestionable omnipotence? No sooner had The Lord said, "Let there be mountains. And let them be huge, massive and bloody gi-normous!", than there were huge, massive and bloody gi-normous mountains!'

'It's nothing,' He murmured modestly. 'Any Supreme Being could do it.'

And we chanted, 'Not only have You made huge, massive and bloody gi-normous mountains appear but, even more incredibly, You have also made our shack completely disappear!'

'What? Have I? I mean, of course I have! It is exactly as I intended! Um, just remind Me, where did I make the shack disappear to?'

'Difficult to tell, but it seems to be under the huge, massive and bloody gi-normous mountains. As if You didn't know.'

'Of course, I knew. Well, I can't stand here all day chit-chatting to you, I've got galaxies to create. So you lot will have to get our shack back.'

'How do we do that, O Lord?'

'It's obvious. Move the mountains!'

'Move the mountains? How? What will move mountains?'

'Faith! Faith will move mountains.'

'But we don't know anyone called Faith.'

'In that case you'll just have to do it yourselves, won't you? Now get on with it, I want those mountains out of here before bedtime!'

Chapter Eleven

The Next 99,999,999,999 Years, Six Months And Twenty-Nine Days... Continued...

o we moved the mountains, exactly 167 yards to the left. And we found the remains of the shack and re-erected it. And at the end of the day, while we were taking a well-earned rest, Himself inspected our work and said, 'Not bad. But I wanted those mountains moved exactly *159* yards to the *right*. Can't I trust you to do the simplest little chore?'

And I said, 'We've been having a chat among ourselves and we've decided that if we're going to spend the next thirty-six thousand, five hundred million, eight hundred and eighteen days lugging huge, massive and bloody gi-normous mountains from one place to another, we need and deserve better working conditions. So we've compiled a list of demands.'

'Demands?'

'Yes, my fellow archangels and I have conferred and we demand an agreement about our terms of employment – the length of the working week, remuneration and, of course, the length and frequency of nectar breaks.

'But even more important than those, I am mandated by my colleagues to bring to Your attention the potentially dangerous situation arising from the low level of ambient lighting. The lack of adequate lighting is appalling. How can my fellow workers and I be expected to move entire mountain ranges in this perpetual gloom? Three times today Comrade Uriel nearly dropped an alp by tripping over one of those pointy things at the top of another mountain. And Comrade Zadkiel nearly had a very nasty accident – almost resulting in a serious wing loss situation – when he slid down that horrible cold white slippery stuff that covers the pointy things. And all because we couldn't see where we were going.

'Frankly, the light from a halo is just not sufficient for the job. If You don't supply some efficient lighting we're refusing to carry on with the work.'

'Refusing!'

'You heard me. We've discussed it and we're all agreed. No light, no work. It's unanimous.'

He looked about Him and his gaze fell on Gabriel.

'You agree with this?'

'Um. Well, "agree" is putting it rather strongly, Let's say that…er…it seems reasonable to me. But, of course, if You've got other ideas…'

Then He turned to Raphael and boomed, 'Are you part of this conspiracy?'

'Lord, I can answer that in two ways.'

'Go ahead.'

'The first way is to say, "No".'

'And the second way?'

'Is to say, "Absolutely, positively and unequivocally no".'

'I'll take that as a negative, then. And what about you, Uriel, and you, Zadkiel?'

And Uriel and Zadkiel looked at Him and opened their mouths and spake, saying, 'Mibbly bomble murgly eeerghft.'

'I see. Well, let's assume that it is not a vote of support for Muriel's demands.'

He looked again upon me. 'So much for unanimity Muriel. In view of your comrades' lack of enthusiasm, do you retract your demand?'

'No.'

CHAPTER ELEVEN

'I see. This is a very serious situation. You have had the audacity to challenge My authority. The authority of The Lord God Almighty, The Supreme And Omnipotent Being! And for it you shall be punished, punished more severely than any being has ever been punished.'

'You're going to turn me back into a toad?'

'Certainly not! This punishment is far, far more severe. This is My judgement on you, Muriel, for your heinous and grievous sin. Henceforth, until the end of time, you shall scrub the kitchen floor.'

The others all gasped. 'You mean, he's got to scrub the kitchen floor as well as do the washing up?'

'That is My command. But that is not the end of it. Because of the grave and unique nature of your crime, I ordain that this very night you, Muriel, will go straight to bed. Without any supper!'

The others fell to wailing, 'No supper! Muriel can't have any ambrosia or nectar! Verily that is a severe and bitter punishment! Not that we're saying he doesn't deserve it, You understand, but we never expected anything as harsh as this. Take pity on Muriel, O Lord! Reconsider Your decision!'

'My mind is made up. And you can consider yourselves lucky that you too are not being punished for defying Me.'

'Thank you, Lord. It wasn't our fault, honest! It was all Muriel's idea. We'll never defy You again. Personally, we'd rather have our legs ripped off and the bleeding stumps hammered up our nostrils than go to bed without any supper!'

He ignored their plaintive screeching and gazed searchingly at me. 'Now, Muriel, what do you have to say for yourself?'

'Ho-hum! It's past my bed time. Good night.'

With that I walked away.

'Oh, Muriel,' He shouted.

I stopped but did not turn to face Him.

'It occurred to Me earlier today that we could do with a bit more light around here, to help us see what we're doing. And so I decided, in My infinite wisdom, of which you may have heard Me speak occasionally, that tomorrow I will create a sun. Just a little idea of My own. Thought I'd let you know. Good night. Sleep tight. And don't forget to say your prayers.'

SATAN

The next morning, after I'd done the washing up and scrubbed the kitchen floor, I joined the rest of the archangels outside. They were staring through the gloom, upwards and into the distance. I followed their gaze and after a few moments I could just make out the tiny figure of Himself, standing aloft one of the pointy things on top of the highest mountain.

As I watched I could just discern Him raising His arm and pointing into the murky blankness of the sky. And from that great distance we could barely hear a still small voice intoning:

Let there be light!

This was followed by the merest suggestion of

Clap!

Flash!

Puff!

'By Jiminy! He's done it one more time! No sooner had The Lord said, "Let there be light!", than there was light!'

Light there was, all around. Above us, in a sky which was now the deepest, purest azure, hung a burnished disc of gold, bathing us in its warm radiance, throwing its welcome rays across the face of Heaven, illuminating every crack and crevice and showing how grubby the bedroom curtains looked.

After a lot of hallelujahing from the others, we returned to our task, moving the mountains exactly 159 yards to the right. But now, because of the unaccustomed heat, we cast aside our frocks and worked stripped to our knickers and bras.

All day long we toiled. And at the end of it, muscles aching and limbs leaden with weariness, we fell gratefully into our beds.

Despite my exhaustion, sleep eluded me. After tossing and turning for an hour I could bear it no longer, so I raised my voice and shouted, 'Somebody forgot to turn the sun off!'

From a nearby room I could hear Him mumbling and grumbling to Himself, followed by the intonation...

'LET THERE BE NIGHT!'

CHAPTER ELEVEN

The click of a finger...

CLAP!
FLASH!
PUFF!

And, lo! There was night.

Chapter Twelve

The Next 99,999,999,999 Years, Six Months And Twenty-Eight Days...

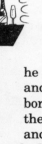

he next 99,999,999,999 years, six months and twenty-eight days passed slowly and boringly. Each morning we were up with the sun and after I'd done the washing up and scrubbed the kitchen floor I joined the others as we worked at shifting one of His latest creations from this point in the universe, to that point in the universe. And, when He wasn't satisfied that we'd put it in exactly the right position, we humped the bloody thing to yet another point in the universe.

On good days we'd just be shifting oceans and continents around, arranging and rearranging them according to His whim. On bad days we'd have to struggle to haul an entire galaxy halfway through space and back again. And when we finally got it into the position that suited His fastidious eye, He'd complain because one planet wasn't exactly and precisely aligned with another, or because one measly little asteroid had got chipped in the move.

And on every single one of these thirty-six thousand, five hundred million, eight hundred and seventeen days I thought of my encounter with Cesspit. But never once did I feel a 'stirring'. To add to my misery, the food became even worse, due to the fact that He had less time to do any cooking.

It must have been on the thirty-six thousand, five hundred million, eight hundred and fifteenth day – or was it the thirty-six thousand, five hundred million and sixteenth day? – I can't remember precisely as one was so like another. Except that on this particular day I had one of my ideas. It was an idea that made all of my other ideas seem like passing fancies.

I was working alone, pushing, I seem to recall, a minor planet called Hilda (damn stupid name for a planet, but when you've created the countless billions that He'd churned out, you tend to lose inspiration) from the outer extremity of the star system of Gavin Minor and into the orbit of the giant sun, Tiddles – where, according to Him, it would make a pleasing and amusing visual counterpoint to some dreary little moon He'd knocked out earlier – when I thought to myself, this is not the sort of work that an archangel should be doing.

I stopped for a moment to catch my breath. And it occurred to me that there must be a better way of getting a planet from one place to another without physically shoving it. So I hovered there, regarding Hilda, and wondered, just wondered whether...

I closed my eyes, took a deep breath, and intoned...

'LET THIS
BLOODY THING
BE MOVED!'

And I opened my eyes. And lo! The bloody thing had not moved. Oh well, it was just an idea. But wait a moment, hadn't I forgotten something?

I closed my eyes again, took another deep breath and reintoned:

'LET THIS
BLOODY THING
BE MOVED!'

And this time I clicked my fingers.
And there was a *CLAP!* of thunder.
A *FLASH!* of lightning.
And a *PUFF!* of smoke.
Admittedly not quite such an impressive

CLAP!

or

FLASH!

or

PUFF!

as He achieved, but not bad for a beginner.

I opened my eyes and looked. And lo! No sooner had I said, 'Let this bloody thing be moved!', than the bloody thing was moved!

It was moved about eighteen inches. A trifle disappointing, but encouraging for an apprentice finger-clicker.

I spent all the rest of that day practising. By the end, I had not only succeeded in moving the planet across vast distances at will, but I'd also discovered I possessed the power to create things.

Nothing very impressive to start with, but I was still discovering the extent of my powers.

It began with me intoning:
'LET THERE BE...UM...LET ME THINK...WELL, ROCK!'

And lo! There was not rock. At least nothing that I recognized as a hard, stony, jagged thing that could be hurled at me.

Instead, there was the most appalling and unbearably loud noise in my ears which sounded as though a hundred trillion parakeets were having their livers pulled out through their backsides while at the same time shrieking, 'Yeah, baby, shake my love pump!,' to a tune that sounded vaguely similar

CREATION WORK SHEET

JOB No:	ARCHANGEL:	DAY:
790561116	Muriel	36,500,000,815

① wash dishes

② scrub K. floor

③ Move planet 'Hilda' (code 4727/P) from creation depot into orbit around sun 'Tiddles' (code 0028/S) of star system 'Gavin minor' — Place next to moon third (3rd) out on the left (code 9000167204/m) — — see diagram....

Cesspit
Cesspit
Cesspit

moon
9000167204/m

X °
Hilda goes here

other moons

Tiddles

SIGNED:	CHECKED:
God	

to Raphael's 'Let's All Praise His Name'. I had to count that as a miserable failure.

Next I intoned:

'LET THERE BE SOMETHING TO DRINK THAT ISN'T NECTAR!'

And lo! there *was* something to drink that very definitely *wasn't* nectar. At that time I didn't know what it was, but it made me feel good, if slightly giddy, and the bubbles got up my nose.

With this feeling of elation, I became emboldened and started plucking words out of the air.

'LET THERE BE…ER…SPINACH!'

And lo! There was spinach. Tons and tons of the stuff, drifting round and round me, green and slimy and revolting to the tongue.

'LET THERE *NOT* BE SPINACH!'

And lo!, to my incredible relief, there was *not* spinach. In quick succession I created thermal underwear with reinforced gusset, cowpats and caviar, which looked remarkably like fish eggs and tasted rather less delicious than cowpats but considerably nicer than spinach.

Finally, as supper time approached, I became so emboldened by my success that I intoned:

'LET THERE BE "STIRRINGS"!'

But, alas, 'stirrings' there were not. I came to the regretful conclusion that I was not omnipotent. But comforted myself that I possessed abilities above and beyond those of the other archangels. Which made me the second most powerful being in the entire universe. This was to be my secret until such time as I could put my powers to good use.

I returned to Heaven, where they were just finishing supper.

'You're too late,' said Gabriel. 'We've eaten all the yummy nectar and ambrosia!'

'I'm not hungry, I ate earlier.'

'Pardon?'

CHAPTER TWELVE

'Er...when I say I ate earlier, what I mean is...um...'

But I was interrupted by Himself, who pushed back His chair, rapped on the table with His spoon and declared, 'Now listen carefully, I have something important to say. I've spent the last thirty-six thousand, five hundred million, eight hundred and fifteen – or possibly sixteen – days creating things of wonder and delight that I have scattered, with your help, hither and yon across the universe. My Really Triff And Absolutely Brill Plan is almost at an end.

'Only one last project remains. A project I shall start upon tomorrow. It will be My greatest feat of creation so far and I'm going to need all My strength so I'm off to bed. In the morning I start on The Big One!'

With that He strode out. Only to return a moment later.

'All right, own up, who's moved the stairs?'

Chapter Thirteen

t last we have reached the thirteenth chapter! And as thirteen is my very favourite number, I thought I'd take this opportunity to break off from my extraordinarily interesting and fascinating narrative and devote this part of the book to sharing with you the long list of my other very favourite things.

What I love more than anything are:

> 1.   Slugs and snails and puppy dogs' tails. Preferably on toast. And washed down with Babycham, made, of course, from real[33]

CHAPTER THIRTEEN

33. Unfortunately, the rest of this chapter has been lost. In fact, it was eaten by the second editor (see Publisher's Warning on page 7). Although not ourselves superstitious, we feel that on this occasion the number...well, that number between twelve and fourteen...has proved unlucky for The Author. Not that we believe in such mumbo jumbo. We apologize for this omission. It will not occur again. Fingers crossed and touch wood.

Chapter Fourteen
The Big One

he next morning we all awoke bright-eyed and bushy-winged and gathered in the kitchen where Himself was to reveal The Big One. Standing on His box He addressed us, 'Having created the universe and all that is in it, I am now ready to embark on My masterpiece, the ultimate creation that will be the monument to My omnipotence. I am about to make the perfect planet – it will be the most beautiful I have yet designed, incorporating all the best bits of the other planets and yet going far, far further, for this one will have things that the others do not – things like assorted greengroceries and myriad life forms, ranging from the humblest creeping thing to the most sophisticated being in the entire universe, excepting us, of course.

'To prove My complete and utter omnipotence, I am going to undertake this enormous scheme without any assistance from you. I shall create this wondrous planet single-handed! Furthermore, and with all due modesty, to show that I am the most powerful Being in existence, I shall complete this vast endeavour in only six – count 'em – just six days!'

CHAPTER FOURTEEN

The others started running around, 'hallelujahing', praising His name and, secretly, jumping for joy at having a six-
day holiday.

Having made His announcement, He changed into His
overalls, jumped into His Chariot of Fire and roared off across
the sky to commence His ultimate work.

That day – the first day of Earth's creation – passed pleas-
antly. The others lounged lazily around, doing nothing, and I,
after I had clicked my fingers and completed the washing up
and floor scrubbing, stole away privately to practise my new
powers, conjuring many more amazing things out of thin air.
Mostly amazing things that I could eat and drink.

I returned late to the shack, tired but happy and very, very
full, to find the others moaning and groaning that there
wasn't any supper and they'd had to make do with stale
ambrosia sandwiches because Himself had not yet returned
from His day's labours. They were in such a bad mood that
they barely sang sixty desultory verses of 'Let's All Praise His
Name Even Though He Hasn't Bothered To Make Our
Dinner And Our Stomachs Feel Like Our Throats Have Been
Cut' before deciding to call it a day and go to bed.

It was in the small hours of the morning that we were
awakened by His voice. He summoned us into His bedroom
and when we were all collected, He gave us a progress report
on His efforts so far.

It seems that He had somewhat over-estimated His powers.
After working all day and half the night, He had not fulfilled
His schedule. In fact, all He had accomplished was to form a
pleasingly globular planet which lacked certain of the el-
ements He had designed – like continents, land masses,
oceans and seas.

Beckoning us closer He whispered that, as He was somewhat late in His time-table, He was offering us the privilege
of helping Him in His great work. But He swore us to secrecy,
saying that we were never, ever to tell a soul that He had had
help. This we promised solemnly to do, given that there
wasn't another soul to tell, even if we'd wanted to.

He then drew out a list headed 'Things To Be Done'. The
first item – 'Have Breakfast' – and the second, 'Make Nice
Round Planet', were crossed off, but all of the other notes

remained and the list stretched from there to eternity and back again.

He explained that He had reassessed the position and decided each of us was to play an important role. Gabriel was to be responsible for putting all the twiddly bits – like mountains, ravines and tundra – on the continents after He had formed them. Raphael was in charge of all stretches of water below the size of major oceans. Uriel would help with various greengrocery items including moss and lichens, the smaller and less gaudy flowers and the duller root vegetables. Zadkiel was to be second-in-command of life forms from amoeba up to and including, but not greater than, moths. Anything more spectacular would, of course, be left to Him. And I...I was to go behind them, cleaning, scrubbing, dusting, polishing and generally clearing up the mess they made.

Looking at the list, Gabriel said, 'While not wishing to question Your wisdom which, as we all know because You have frequently mentioned it – but not so frequently as to appear boastful, honest – is infinite, do You still think we'll be able to accomplish all this in only five days?'

He answered, 'I've thought of that. Tell Me, how many hours are there in a day?'

'Twenty-four,' we chorused.

'And which idiot arbitrarily decided that each day should contain only twenty-four hours?'

'You did!'

'Yes, well, I'm sure I had a good reason for it at the time. But now I am ordaining that each day will consist of four hundred and seventy-six hours, and that only three of them shall be night. That should be enough to get the job done. Now, I'm going upstairs for My three hours sleep, after which we'll start on the job in earnest.'

We reminded Him that there wasn't an upstairs and that He was already in His bedroom. He reminded us that He didn't need reminding about anything, being omniscient. So we said good-night and didn't dare remind Him to set His alarm clock.

Sixteen hours later He leapt from His bed and resumed the great enterprise. And thus did we create the Earth and all that's on it in only five days plus the one that He'd already wasted. Which were really ninety-nine days, taking into account that one of His new days equalled nineteen of His old days.[34]

Every day we toiled at our tasks. Or, rather, the others toiled while I went behind them, looking at the mess they'd left, clicking my fingers and saying, 'LET THERE NOT BE MESS!' And lo! there was *not* mess. This left me four hundred and seventy-five hours and fifty-five minutes a day to occupy myself as best I could.

The days passed peacefully until the fourth when, at about half past 227 o'clock in the afternoon, we heard a sound like thunder, which we knew wasn't thunder as we had not yet got around to creating weather, and therefore must be Himself having one of His tantrums. We dropped whatever we were doing – painful for Gabriel who was just fixing a large pointy thing to the top of Mont Blanc which crashed on his toe – and rushed (or, in Gabriel's case, hobbled) across the partially completed planet to join Him.

He was standing atop the highest mountain which we called Mount Duvet but which later became Everest and He said, 'I've just been making a tour of inspection and I'm not a happy God, not a happy God at all. Gabriel! You are responsible for putting all the twiddly bits on to the continents I've created. By and large I concede that you've done a good job, but will you explain to Me what that is yonder?'

Gabriel turned to look and said, 'That's a mountain.'

'It certainly looks like a mountain, but why is smoke pouring from the top of it?'

'I...er...d-don't kn-know,' Gabriel stammered, 'it wasn't like that when I last looked. It was just like any other mountain and it w-w-wasn't sp-sp-spewing smoke and rock and molten lava.'

'Which is pouring all over My beautiful clean glacier, causing it to melt and drip into My newly-created and perfectly-

---

34. We would just like to point out that we think it's a pretty amazing feat that God managed to create the Earth and all that's on it in ninety-nine days, even if He did have some assistance. In fact, absolutely and incredibly amazing considering how long it takes a plumber to turn up to fix a dripping tap.

formed Gobi desert. There's no point in having a desert if it's full of water. Muriel, go and clear it up before it turns into another swamp, of which we already have more than a sufficiency.'

Gabriel looked downcast and said, 'I'm very sorry, I suppose I must have got the ingredients mixed up.'

Himself then turned to Raphael, saying, 'You are in charge of all stretches of water below the size of major oceans, can you explain what's gone wrong with that one?'

Raphael looked at the small-ish sea in question and answered, 'It looks all right to me.'

'It may look all right but try tasting it.'

Raphael dipped in his finger and licked it. 'Grooh!', he yelped.

'Grooh, indeed! How much salt did you put in there?'

'Exactly the amount in the recipe You gave me – one heaped tablespoon for every hundred gallons.'

'Well, it tastes as though you poured an entire barrel into that. It's so salty that nothing will live in there.

'And speaking of living things, Uriel, you've been given the task of helping Me with the greengroceries, kindly tell me what this nasty little object is?'

'That?' said Uriel. 'Why, that's a mushroom.'

'Oh. Is it?'

'Yes, You remember, it was on Your list between Muscatel and Mustard.'

'Yes, yes, of course I remember. And I suppose this is a quite adequate...er...mushroom. It's just that I expected it to be, well, shinier. I'll overlook that for the moment and turn to Zadkiel who is second-in-command of life forms from amoeba up to and including, but not greater than, moths. Tell Me, Zadkiel, what is this?'

He opened His hand and revealed a small creature crawling across His palm. Zadkiel peered at it and said, 'That? Why, that's...er...um...a hippopotamus.'

'You're guessing, aren't you? That is not a hippopotamus, which resembles a "sofa" with teeth and which I finished creating not half-an-hour ago. So what is this?'

'Um...is it by any chance a bunny rabbit?'

'No it is not. A bunny rabbit is a fluffy furry creature with

CHAPTER FOURTEEN

a pom-pom tail and a little twitchy nose. While this, this...
THING, is small and wriggly and slimy and squirmy and
horrible! So what is it?'

'I don't know,' Zadkiel admitted woefully, 'but it's eating
that mushroom.'

And as we watched, the small, wriggly, slimy, squirmy,
horrible thing took a large bite out of the mushroom, swallow-
ed, belched, rolled over and lay motionless on its back.

Chapter Fifteen
The Big Bang

 hey stared at it in a stunned silence. Eventually, Himself said, 'What has happened to the small, wriggly, squirmy, slimy, horrible thing?' And I said, 'That thing is a slug. It ate the mushroom which isn't a mushroom but a toadstool and as a result it has poisoned itself and died.'

'Slug?' said Himself. 'What's a slug? I don't remember ordering anything called a slug. And what's this "toadstool"? I'm sure that wasn't on My list.'

'No,' I replied, 'neither of them were on Your list. I created them, along with the smoking mountain, which is a volcano, and the sea with too much salt in which nothing can live and which I call the Dead Sea.'

Again His voice was like thunder.

'You created them? You!'

'Yes, me!'

'How did you create these things?'

'The same way You do. I just close my eyes, think of a word, any word like, for example, "spider" and say "LET THERE BE SPIDER!" Then I click my fingers and...'

CHAPTER FIFTEEN

CLAP!
FLASH!
PUFF!

'Lawksamercy,' cried the archangels, 'Muriel can do it too! No sooner did he say, "Let there be spider!" than lo! there is...well...a nasty creepy-crawly thing with lots of hairy legs. And we don't like it!' They picked their skirts up and scuttled behind Himself for protection. Himself yielded not a step. He stood there, glaring at me.

'SO, MURIEL,' He thundered, 'YOU'VE FINALLY DIS-COVERED THAT YOU TOO POSSESS POWERS, BUT WHY ARE YOU USING THEM TO CREATE NASTY SQUIGGLY, SQUIRMY AND HAIRY-LEGGED THINGS?

WHY ARE YOU ABUSING YOUR GIFTS TO CREATE VOLCANOES, POISONOUS PLANTS AND OTHER ABOMI-NATIONS?'

'Everybody should have a hobby.'

'A HOBBY! YOU CALL PERVERTING AND DESPOILING MY GREATEST MASTERPIECE A HOBBY!'

'Well, it passes the time. And look at what You've created – fluffy little bunny rabbits and cuddly koalas, pretty flowers which waft scents. It's all so...so *bland*, I thought I'd create some things that were more interesting, more exciting, more dangerous! Things that would add a bit of spice to this depressingly bijou planet.'

He waxed wrathful, more wrathful than I had ever seen Him.

'YOU DARE TO IMPOSE YOUR IDEAS ON MY CREATION?'

'Why not? After all, I am as powerful as you.'

'NO ONE IS AS POWERFUL AS THE SUPREME BEING!'

'I am and I'll prove it. How would you like to be a toad?'

'I WARN YOU, MURIEL, BE VERY, VERY CAREFUL!'

I closed my eyes, took a very, very deep breath and intoned, 'LET HIM BE A TOAD!'

I clicked my fingers...

CLAP!
FLASH!
PUFF!

Slowly I opened my eyes. And lo! He was *not* a toad.

'Funny,' I said, 'it worked on that hippopotamus earlier. Do you mind if I have another try?'

'MURIEL! THIS IS THE END! YOU ARE FIRED!'

'Fired? You can't fire me! I've got my rights! What about my three months' notice and golden handshake?'

'OH, GO TO HELL!'

'Hell? Where's Hell? Look, as I was saying, you can't fire me because...'

CLAP!
FLASH!
PUFF!

CHAPTER FIFTEEN

...I'm qu
            i
             i
              i
               i
                i
                 i
                  i
                   i
                    i
                     i
                      i
                       i
                        i
                         i
                          i
                           i
                            i
                             i
                              i
                               i
                                i
                                 i
                                  i
                                   i
                                    i
                                     i
                                      i
                                       i
                                        i
                                         i
                                          i
                                           i
                                            i
                                             i
                                              i
                                               i
                                                i
                                                 tting!'

Chapter Sixteen

Paradise Lost

hus was I hurled headlong flaming from th'ethereal sky and cast into the bottomless pit.[35]

I soon discovered that the pit wasn't bottomless when I hit the bottom of it with the top of me. When I regained consciousness I found myself in the darkest darkness I'd ever seen. Or not seen. I couldn't understand why it took my eyes so long to adjust to the stygian gloom, until I realized that I didn't have the light from my halo. Indeed, I didn't have a halo at all. And I didn't have a silly white frock either. Nor a huge flapping pair of plaid wings.

But I still had my fingers, so I said 'LET THERE BE LIGHT!', clicked them and a huge pillar of fire leapt in front of me. As the flames danced, spouted and licked into the air I could just make out a massive pair of adamantine gates.

---

35. This passage owes something to Milton's *Paradise Lost*. In fact, it owes everything to that epic poem. The Author claims it is a parody of Milton and directs us to his monograph, *Parodies Regained*.

Impaled on top of them was a grimacing skull, gaping in the rictus grin of one who has died in unimaginable torment. Under it hung a sign with words daubed in blood:-

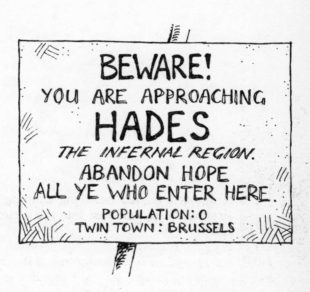

Involuntarily a shiver ran down my spine, the hairs on the back of my head prickled and I felt my knees tremble. I turned away but was met by a wall of blank darkness. There was nowhere to go but forward. Fearfully, I walked towards the gates, my footsteps ringing hollow in the terrible dead silence. I came abreast of those huge, forbidding gates and pushed them with quivering hand.

At first they resisted my touch but then slowly, menacingly slowly, they yielded, swinging open with a mournful creaking groan. I crossed the threshold and entered the abyss. No sooner had I set foot on the other side of the gates than all Hell broke loose.

Where can I find the words to describe that sound? It was like nothing I'd ever heard. It seemed to come from deep within the maw of that fathomless darkness, rising, ever rising, in a thin, curdling shriek, at first utterly incomprehensible, assaulting my agonized ears.

I cowered beneath the awful sound, screaming, 'Which horrible hound of hell is this? Reveal yourself!'

Finally my tortured ears discerned the blood-chilling message: 'Hello! Prescott's the name, Rodney Prescott.'

From the nightmare darkness a grotesque apparition emerged, thrusting its deathly white hand towards me. Clutched in the skeletal fingers was a card. Fearfully I snatched it from the grisly claw.

RODNEY PRESCOTT

SENIOR PARTNER

ORDURE, ORDURE, FILTH, SLIME AND PRESCOTT

ESTATE AGENTS

'So you finally turned up,' he said, 'I've been waiting since the Thursday before Time Immemorial. Anyway, now you're here, let me give you a quick tour of the place. As you can see, it is a superior and highly desirable residence, set in millions of acres of rolling countryside and affording the most idyllic vistas on all sides. The main living (if it can be called living) area measures one hundred and forty-three thousand miles wide by two hundred and fifty-nine thousand miles long (that, of course, is into the bay window), having the benefit of fitted carpets throughout.

'This unique dwelling combines a wealth of original features plus the very latest in mod cons, including central heating, jacuzzi, integral garage, fitted wardrobes and kitchen units,

bathroom en suite with low-level flush cistern and matching vanitory units in desirable avocado green.'

I cast around me. 'I can't see any of those things.'

'No, well, that's just estate agents' jargon. Or, to use the technical term, bare-faced lies. You haven't encountered lies before but you'll get used to them. To be brutally frank, it doesn't have any of those things. All right, the place doesn't look much but with a little flair, a good builder and extensive renovation and refurbishment it does have enormous potential. Given enough imagination and money, you could turn it into a cosy little purgatory.

'Look, why don't I leave you the keys and allow you to browse. Don't hurry, you've got all the time in the Underworld. Now, if you'll excuse me, I must rush, I understand there's shortly to be a boom in land sales on Earth – a lot of development in the suburbs of Eden – and I don't want to miss out.'

Before I could ask about the rateable value, main drains and closeness of bus routes, he had disappeared, leaving me alone. Utterly alone in this vast, desolate wasteland.

I had nothing – no status, no friends, no comfort. Nothing at all, except this derelict wilderness and a burning ache in my heart for revenge against He who had stripped me of everything and cast me into the loathsome void.

As I wandered, abandoned and solitary, through the echoing caverns of this inhospitable region I realized that for the very first time in my long existence I was happy!

Yes, ecstatically, deliriously happy!

I rushed back through the numberless chambers of Hell, back to those huge grim gates and ripped down the 'For Sale' notice.

Hades was mine!

It wasn't much of a place, but it was home. And I had plans for it.

Chapter Seventeen
Home Sweet Home

ooking back over the millennia it's difficult for me to remember exactly what Hades was like when I moved in. It has changed so much since then.

In those days it was just a little hell-hole, nothing fancy, but somewhere to hang my hate (as it were). Since then it has grown and expanded and improved to become what it is today – The Hades Leisure Park, incorporating The Hellfire Club and Inferno-A-Go-Go Disco (a wholly-owned subsidiary of Hellton Hotels Inc.).

Right from the start I intended to set up a rival attraction to Heaven. Somewhere that was not run, as He ran His place, like a boy scouts camp but somewhere you could, if you so wished, scout for camp boys, not to mention willing girls and every animal of every possible gender, all in a constant state of sexual arousal.

My kingdom was going to provide everything that His did not, which left a lot of scope considering that Heaven offers very little apart from infinite harp recitals. You need the patience of a saint to endure it, which explains why it is populated almost entirely by saints and some of the duller popes and prelates who didn't have the imagination to try The Seven Delightful Sins before condemning them. (Mind you, we can boast more than our fair share of pontiffs down here, especially those from the heydays of the Middle Ages when they spread their message of brotherly love in more physical ways. Not to mention sisterly love and, indeed, love with people outside their immediate family circle. Pontiffs like Pope Urbane who could do things with a Papal Bull that surprised even me. And absolutely astonished the beast in question.)

It must be some measure of our success that The Great Fraud and His followers have spent so much effort spreading lies and propaganda about my little enterprise. All that nonsense about thumbscrews, racks and red-hot pokers!

Certainly we have them, but only for those whose taste runs to such pleasures. If you don't relish torture – either receiving or inflicting it – nobody is going to force you. (Well, all right, old Sacher de Masoch might try to force you, but that's just his way. If you don't want to play, simply knee him in the groin. He adores it. And when he begs and pleads for more, emulate de Sade: watch him squirm and grovel and absolutely refuse to pander to his needs. The Marquis really has raised cruelty to a peak of sophistication.)

We realize not everyone wants to gouge out the eyes or flay the flesh of his fellow man. Some prefer to do it to dumb animals, and who are we to say they are wrong? (Incidentally, I'm reliably informed that such pratices are common on Earth under the pretence of medical research. Naturally, this sort of behaviour does not appeal to the animal lovers among us who prefer dumb creatures to perform experiments on them, particularly stallions and German shepherds. The dogs, that is, not the human variety who remain faithful to their sheep.)

If, for some bizarre and squeamish reason, you do not wish to participate in these pleasant diversions, there are so many other ways to pass Infinity. For example, there is Pro-Am Pillaging and Looting in which you are invited to lay waste to large tracts of countryside under the tutelage of Genghis Khan. (Regrettably, ravishing has been dropped from this event due to an unfortunate and acutely embarrassing personal problem which I won't specify. Let's just say that not for nothing is he known as Genghis Khan't.)

Also on offer is Celebrity Plundering in which you can ransack entire cities under the supervision of royalty among who we are proud to list 'Mad' King Ludwig of Bavaria, 'Insane' Prince Francis of Ruthenia and 'Completely Loony' Duke Darren of Walloonia who is under the impression that he is a chipolata.[36]

Fortunately, being a six-foot cocktail sausage doesn't prevent Darren from plundering with the best of them. And probably the very best of them is dear old Ivan the Terrible, one of the all-time great plunderers who got his nickname for much the same reason as Genghis got his. (Ask Catherine the Great why Ivan is Terrible. And ask any of our several million clients who have shared her bed why Catherine is Great.) But enough of Ivan's shortcomings – so to speak – they are more than compensated for by the rampant satyrism of his son, Ivan the Amazing, and nephew Ivan the Really Brain-Explodingly Fantastic.[37]

There are so many ways in which you can while away your time and when, after a long day, you return tired, happy and gore-spattered after some enthusiastic Synchronized Vandalism (desecrate churches and deface the world's greatest works of art to your favourite Nazi marches under the tuition of a qualified Visigoth, packed lunch included), you'll probably want to soothe away the cares of the day in a relaxing hot bloodbath, gorge yourself to bursting in one of our many restaurants (one to suit every palate from vegan, where only the freshest vegetables are eaten, to cannibal where only the freshest vegans are eaten) and curl up for a few hours with a really bad book. We have the largest library of erotica in the universe, not to mention an unparalleled selection of pornographic films and videos, showing sexual acts that will make the eyes pop out of your head.

36. Among our clients Ludwig is also known as the 'Mad' Queen of Bavaria, due to his fondness for our male members. And, indeed, all male members whether or not they belong to patrons of our club.

37. Not to be confused with his identical twin brother, Igor the So-So. Although many of our female clients have confused them and been very disappointed as a result.

And so to bed. Where you can bonk yourself brainless with one of the great courtesans or legendary studs of history. Or both. And perform sexual acts that will make the eyes pop out of your head. Literally.

But what if you become bored rigid by being bored rigid (as we amusingly put it)? No problem! There are so many other entertainments to divert you.

If you wish for a quiet, contemplative evening you could play Diabolic Scrabble (only obscene words accepted) with Machiavelli but, be warned, he cheats. Or join the art class where you'll be taught how to forge some of the world's greatest masterpieces, to be destroyed the next day by the Synchronized Vandals. Or you can just retire to the Smoking Room (next to the Smouldering Room and along the corridor from the Bursting Into Flames Room – no ladies admitted since one was singed by a masochist who set fire to himself; she caused the most terrible fuss – Hell hath no fury like a woman scorched) and enjoy a Bloody Mary, or the non-alcoholic version, a Bloody Tee-Totaller, made from a freshly-slaughtered Mary and Tee-Totaller respectively. As you sip your favourite tipple you can browse through *Helle* magazine to discover what the well-dressed thrill-seeker is wearing, or, rather, having ripped off their willing body this season. Or you can put your feet up on a poof and watch hellevision which keeps you in touch with news of the upper world's latest disasters, catastrophes and holocausts. Or, as we call them, our latest triumphs.

Which other leisure complex in this or any other world could offer you all this? And for so little!

Yes, all this can be yours.

To enjoy the infinite and exquisite pleasures offered by Hades all you have to do is sell me your soul! What a bargain! And to make it even more convenient, I'll buy it on easy terms, stretched over the rest of your life.[38]

38. This offer does not apply to Mrs Elspeth Jenkins, Mr Zigismund Kowalski, Han Wen Yoo, Abdullah Al Akram or The Very Reverend Maurice Gilchrist who, unfortunately, have left it too late. Exactly one minute too late. Goodbye! However, you, Dear Reader, may like to fill in the membership form at the end of this chapter. Assuming, of course, you are not one of the above named.

CHAPTER SEVENTEEN

As I always say, for most things you need Hire Purchase, but to enter the Underworld we offer Lower Purchase! People have been known to die laughing at that joke. And those who don't laugh just die, screaming in agony.

Oh, by the way, this business about the Fiery Furnace. Don't believe everything you hear. Admittedly, it does exist, but it's just a form of central heating like any other. We switched years ago from fuelling it with Souls in Torment. Today we simply shovel in advertising executives. What we describe as a blaze of publicity!

Well, that's given you a peek into Hades as it is in the twentieth century. It is, I'm sure you'll agree, one Hell of a place. So very, very different from the empty, echoing hulk that I inhabited all those eons ago. And what made the difference and started me on my long and highly successful career was my brilliantly simple coup of persuading my first client to eat an apple.

HADES LEISURE PARK

Please enrol me as an After-Life Member of The Hades Leisure Park (incorporating The Hellfire Club and Inferno-A-Go-Go Disco), the premier pleasure complex of this and every other world.

I understand that in exchange for my eternal soul I can enjoy the myriad facilities, perversities and indulgences of The Ultimate Pleasure Dome for the rest of Infinity (or until Armageddon, whichever is sooner.)

I also understand that as soon as my application is accepted The Hades Leisure Park will rush me a FREE GIFT of six bottles of vintage Brimstone.

HOTELS!

HELLFIRE CLUB

PRO-AM PILLAGING

CATHERINE THE GREAT!

DISORDER FORM

Surname ....

  (Mr/Mrs/Miss/Ms/Other : Delete according to gender, marital status, life form)

Anti-Christian names (in full) ....

  Address: House Name or Number ....

    Town/City ....

    Zip or Postcode ....

    Country ....

    Planet ....

    Galaxy ....

    Universe ....

  Signature: ....

  (Beasts make mark here): ....

Complete this coupon and rush it to:
Hades Leisure Park, p.l.c.,
P.O. Box 666
Underworld.

As a member of The Hades Leisure Park I agree not to abide by any of the rules of the club.

MONEY BACK GUARANTEE

If not entirely satisfied with the facilities of Hades within 7 millennia we guarantee that we will not give your money back.

Chapter Eighteen

Nipples Like Ripe Apricots

fter being dumped in Hades, I wandered around my new domain. As I surveyed it, I realized how much needed to be done. The place was in shabby condition, it had been left empty and neglected since The Year Dot and was in need of a great deal of work.[39]

Water dripped down the walls, the wind howled through the roofs, paint flaked and peeled from every surface, fungi sprouted from each crack and the place was pervaded by the sour, rank stench of decay. Looking around, I realized it just wouldn't do. It was far too cosy.

I spent a lot of time making it as squalid and sordid as possible, covering the walls with slime, the floors with sewage and hanging the windows with festoons of rotting entrails. That done, I had mains sulphur piped in to waft its noxious fumes through the chambers.

When I'd finished Hades was the sort of place that would strike dread even into the black hearts of the desperate and despised, the murderous and mad, the vicious and vile who were to be my clients. But when they eventually arrived, they felt instantly at home and kept pestering to know what had happened to the 7.43. I had, quite unwittingly, modelled it on a railway waiting-room.[40]

But my first customers wouldn't arrive for some considerable time (and the train never arrived at all, that's the hell of the place) because there were no customers available except for His archangels and I knew there was no point in trying to tempt them to join me, especially since He'd offered them a whole bundle of incentives to retain their loyalty – including pension scheme, Luncheon Vouchers and company chariots. This narrowed down my potential clientele considerably.

I could barely contain my desire to start on my diabolic career of seducing souls and so, in between re-desecrating Hades, I would pop up to Earth for a recce, to spy out the land and see how His creation was progressing. Obviously, I couldn't just wander around the place in my usual form, but it was

---

39. The Year Dot. Short for The Year Dorothy. Before years were numbered, they were given individual names, which were frequently shortened. The Year Dot was the first, followed by The Year Doug, The Year Dick and The Year Ken. The system had its disadvantages beause people had trouble remembering whether The Year George came before or after The Year Mimi and whether that was preceded or succeeded by The Year Rupert. This method was abandoned in The Year Fiona (or possibly Gerald). It was replaced by a numbering system – The Year Dot became 1, Doug was 2, Dick 3 and so on. However, the numbers weren't actually called one, two, three, etc. As the counting system was based on digits of the hand, the numbering went Thumb, Finger Next To Thumb, Middle Finger and so on through the fingers of both hands. Having run out of fingers, the 11th year was known as Big Toe, the 12th was The Not-Quite-Such-A-Big-Toe Next to Big Toe and so on up to The Little Teeny Weeny Toe On The Left Foot which was 20. This proved moderately satisfactory until New Year's Eve of The Little Teeny Weeny Toe On The Left Foot when it was realized that they had virtually run out of extremities. Thus the 21st year became known as The Sticky-Out Thing That Boys Have But Ladies Don't. After this the system broke down completely and was, in turn, replaced with the one we now recognize.

40. It was after this discovery that I completely re-decorated Hades, turning it into the luxuriously-appointed recreation centre and leisure complex that it now is. However, I've retained one corner of it in the old style for those deeply perverse clients who get their masochistic kicks from waiting for eternity for a train that never arrives. It's next to The Pub With No Beer and just behind The Restaurant That Is Fully Booked Until The End Of Time And Even If It Wasn't, We Wouldn't Admit Riff-Raff Like You.

surprisingly easy to disguise myself and pass unnoticed. They were far too busy to pay any heed to an extra stone lying on the beach or a log that suddenly appeared on the ground.

In these guises I would lurk, watching and waiting for the first signs of some life form that was worth tempting and, when I got bored with trying to seduce sticks, leaves and plankton into the ways of wickedness, I would do a little freelance creating of my own. I derived quite a bit of pleasure from hearing one or other of the archangels letting out a scream and shrieking, 'Euggghhh! Who put these disgusting leathery wings on this mouse? And why is it sucking the blood out of that dear little antelope I spent all yesterday afternoon creating?' Or, 'Which idiot took all the legs off this lizard? And whose idea was it to put this rattle on its tail?'

At night I'd skulk outside the shack disguised as a shrub, eavesdropping on their conversation to discover what effects my latest creations had had.

'Gabriel,' Raphael would say, 'you know that nice black and white animal I made that looks a bit like a badger but isn't? Well, guess what? Today I went to inspect it to see if its fur was sticking snugly to its body and when I approached it, it gave off this most appalling pong. It really stank! I'm sure that smelling like a rancid herring wasn't in the original blueprint.'

And Gabriel would reply, 'You think you've got trouble! I've just been combing my silky golden hair and look what I've found – there are millions of little white scaly bits in it! Look, the stuff is all over my nice clean frock.'

And Uriel would chime in, 'Attisshoo! Oh! I'b hab dem for days. Dat's nobbing combared wid habing you dose bunged ub and consdandly sneeding. Attisshoo! I feel like death warbed ub.'

And Zadkiel would pause for a moment from squeezing the pus out of the boils that had so suddenly and inexplicably erupted on his face and say, 'You know, this place isn't entirely turning out as I expected. But I suppose when you're doing a job this big, you've got to expect the odd hiccup.'

And Raphael would say, 'Hic! What's a hic-hic-hiccup? And hic has any-hic-body got a cure for whatever it hic is that keeps making me go hic?'

CHAPTER EIGHTEEN

Himself noticed nothing amiss because He was too intent on the other side of Earth creating His masterwork. He called it Eden and He was fashioning it single-handedly, moulding and shaping it to become the most beautiful place He had ever created. It was a riot of multi-coloured blooms and succulent fruits, of dancing fountains and lush verdant palms. The leaves sparkled in the constant sunlight, dappling the paths beneath. The breeze sighed and riffled, gently stirring the limpid water of the pools where brightly-coloured carp rose to splash the rippled surface. Here a lamb gambolled giddily, there a fawn frisked and frolicked while nearby a kitten skittered through the orchids; above it a turtle dove cooed and a nightingale warbled its liquid notes into the scented sky.

It was a feast for the eyes, a symphony for the ears, a bouquet for the nostrils and a joy for the heart. It was, in short, utterly repellent.

But under the watchful eyes of Himself there was little I could do to exercise my demonic powers, except smuggle in the odd aphid, weevil and thrip to munch His roses. And the occasional mole to flaw His perfect lawns.

Instead I bided my time, watching and waiting until the moment I could fulfil my destiny. And that moment came at exactly 238 o'clock in the afternoon of the fifth day when He called His archangels to Him. They came running from all corners of the planet and gathered about Him in the middle of Eden. He ordered them to sit on a nearby log while He revealed His final and ultimate intention.

And so it was that as they sat – and as I groaned silently under their weight – He declared unto them: 'I am now ready to perform My final and greatest act of creation. Yea, even though I have already created a myriad profusion of breath-taking wonders entirely single-handed, except for a little help with the menial chores that we need not mention outside this circle, this last creation will make them seem like cheap conjuring tricks. The time has come for me to fashion a creature called Man, which I will create in My image, after My likeness.'

So saying, He stooped to the ground and scooped together a handful of dust. The archangels, entranced and trembling with anticipation, leaned forward to gaze at the little mound.

'From this meagre dust will spring the acme of My creation.'

He closed His eyes, drew in His breath and intoned:

'LET THIS DUST BE MAN. AND LET THIS MAN BE MADE IN MY IMAGE, AFTER MY LIKENESS!'

CLAP!

FLASH!

AT-TISSHOOOO!

A still, small voice said, 'I'b terridly soddy.'

'URIEL! YOU'VE BLOWN AWAY MY GREATEST CREATION! HOW MANY TIMES HAVE I COMMANDED YOU, IF YOU'RE GOING TO SNEEZE, USE A HANDKER-CHIEF?'

'Neber. You neber told be dat.'

'NO, WELL, IT NEVER SEEMED IMPORTANT BEFORE. NOW, IF YOU CAN CONTROL YOUR NOSTRILS, I WILL START ALL OVER AGAIN. AND THIS TIME I REQUIRE COMPLETE SILENCE!'

Once more He stooped. Once more He scooped together a handful of dust. Once more He closed His eyes and drew in His breath. And once more He intoned:

'LET THIS DUST BE MAN. AND LET THIS MAN BE MADE IN MY IMAGE, AFTER MY LIKENESS!'

CLAP!
FLASH!
PUFF!

Chapter Nineteen
Quivering Buttocks[41]

When the smoke had cleared, the archangels leaned forward again and gazed at His final creation. As one they raised their voices and exulted: 'We just don't believe this, even though we've seen it with our own eyes! No sooner did God say, "LET THIS DUST BE MAN" than, lo! this dust *was* man!

'And not only that, but no sooner did God say, "AND LET THIS MAN BE MADE IN MY IMAGE, AFTER MY LIKENESS!" than, lo!, he *was* made after His image, after His likeness! For lo!, this man is only five feet two inches tall and is wearing a bright orange wig!'

Thus was Adam created.

41. The publishers would like to apologize for the misleading titles of the last two chapters. Chapter Nineteen should have been headed 'Eden' and not 'Nipples Like Ripe Apricots'. This chapter should be titled 'Adam', and not as printed above. These changes were made at the last moment by The Author for his own nefarious purposes. We are confident that no other such amendments have crept into the silky blonde triangle of her tantalizing pubic mound.

And Himself raised Adam up to his feet. And Adam put one foot in front of the other and took his first halting steps on Earth. He walked straight into a palm tree, turned, tripped over a stone and fell headlong into a limpid pool. Himself dragged Adam from the water, raised him to his feet again but this time adjusted his wig so that it was not on back to front and so Adam could see where he was going. He blinked in the light and took his first look at Eden. He gazed around him at the riotous profusion of blooms and fruits, at the dancing fountains, the gambolling lamb, the frolicking fawn, at the cooing turtle dove and the warbling nightingale. He drank all this in, then he opened his mouth and uttered his first words on Earth: 'I'm bursting for a pee.'

Then he urinated over the orchids.

Himself turned to the archangels and spake unto them, saying, 'I think I've made a terrible mistake.' He then drew them to Him and said, 'I know I said that the creation of Man was to be My final act of creation, but looking at this shambling moron, I think I'll have one more try.'

So saying, He lightly flicked Adam on the back of the head with His finger, causing his wig to fly off and his body to slump to the ground in a coma. As Adam lay there, Himself plucked a rib from his body and held it aloft, saying, 'Behold I have plucked this rib from Adam.'

And Gabriel said, 'Behold He has plucked a rib. Um...can you eat it?'

And Himself said, 'As a matter of fact, you can. It's delicious with barbecue sauce.'

So they made a fire, cooked the rib and ate it.

Then Himself leant over Adam again and plucked another rib, saying, 'He'll never miss it.'

He held the second rib aloft, saying, 'Behold this other rib I have plucked from Adam. From this I will fashion My final and My greatest creation. From this will I fashion Woman.'

He closed His eyes, drew in His breath and intoned:

'LET THIS RIB BE WOMAN!'

CLAP!
FLASH!

CHAPTER NINETEEN

'Hang on! Wait a second! I haven't finished yet!
'LET THIS RIB BE WOMAN. AND LET HER *NOT* BE MADE IN MY IMAGE, AFTER MY LIKENESS!'

PUFF!

And when the smoke cleared, the archangels exulted once more, chanting, 'Hallelujah! No sooner did God say, "LET THIS RIB BE WOMAN AND LET HER *NOT* BE MADE IN MY IMAGE, AFTER MY LIKENESS" than lo!, there *was* woman and she is most definitely and decidedly *not* made in His image, in His likeness!'

'Behold!', quoth Gabriel, 'her stature; she must be well over six feet tall!'

'Behold!', quoth Raphael, 'her fine blonde hair which is like unto spun gold!'

'Behold!', quoth Uriel, 'the alabaster whiteness and lustrous sheen of her silken skin!'

'Behold!' quoth Zadkiel, 'the enormous pair of knockers on her!'

And I did behold her and saw that she was tall and blonde and creamy-skinned and had an enormous pair of knockers. And I felt a 'stirring'. A 'stirring' such as I'd never felt before. And as I gazed at the perfection that was Eve, I felt an overwhelming desire, a desire to seduce this exquisite creature. As I stared into her cornflower blue eyes, I knew I had met my destiny.

My reverie was ruined by the sound of four archangels' bums crashing to the ground. 'Blimey!', said Gabriel, 'I could have sworn this log just stirred.'

Chapter Twenty
Rude Bits[42]

Himself extended His hand to Eve and gently led her to the recumbent form of Adam, who lay on the ground, snoring loudly and scratching his groin. Himself blew in Adam's ear to wake him. When that had no effect, He shook his shoulder. Eventually, He managed to wake the Man by kicking him hard in the ribs.

'OWWWWWWW! That bloody well hurt!' He clutched his sides, saying, 'I don't know what was going on while I was asleep, but I feel completely plucked.'

And Himself presented Eve to Adam saying, 'This woman have I created to be your helpmeet and soulmate, your comfort and your wife. You shall cleave unto your wife and you shall be one flesh.'

And Adam replied, saying, 'Cut out all the poncey talk. I

---

42. We apologize for this chapter heading. This is obviously another attempt by The Author to create mischief and to mislead the reader. This chapter should be titled, 'Adam And Eve'.

didn't understand half of that but I will say one thing, this Eve's got a nice pair of knockers on her.'

Eve smiled sweetly and in a voice like molten honey crooned, 'I shall be your helpmeet and soulmate, your comfort and your wife. I shall cleave unto you and we shall be one flesh.'

And Adam smiled at Eve, saying, 'And I shall cleave unto you and we shall be one flesh. Now, what do you say to a quick leg-over?'

Himself said, 'Verily, I have created vegetables with a greater intellectual capacity than this gibbering dimwit. Desist this babbling and come with Me as I show you the glories of My creation which I have fashioned just for you.'

Eve took Adam's hand in hers and they walked slowly side by side through Eden, pausing now and again for her to admire the beauty that surrounded them and for him to urinate over it.

Finally, God led them to a secluded arbour and there He showed them a tree. He spake unto them, saying, 'Of every tree of the garden thou mayest freely eat. But thou shalt *not* eat of the fruit of this tree.'

And Adam said, 'Come again?'

So Himself spake again, 'Look, you cabbage-brained cretin, it's quite simple. You can stuff yourself on the fruit of that tree there, you can gorge yourself till you're sick on the fruit of that tree over there. But you cannot and must not lay one finger on the apples from this tree here. Got it? Savvy? Comprenez?'

'All right, I've got it. But what's so special about this tree? Looks the same as all the rest to me.'

'This is The Tree of Good and Evil and I, The Lord Thy God, forbid you to eat its fruit.'

'Fair enough. You're the boss and if You want to save the best fruit for Yourself, I s'pose You're entitled to. But there's no need to spin this fairy tale about The Tree Of Good and Evil. I wasn't born yesterday, you know.'

'Indeed you were not. You were born this very day and it's still not too late for Me to change My mind about your continued existence.'

But Eve soothed Him. 'We understand what You have said and we will obey Your command. Thank You for creating this beautiful place which we will cherish and nurture so that it will further glorify Your name.'

And Himself patted her hand and grinned stupidly, saying, 'Thank you, my dear, you've made an old God very happy. Now, I'm going to run along and leave you two young things alone. Why don't you be fruitful and multiply?' With that He winked at Eve, nudged Adam in the ribs, causing him to howl in pain, and disappeared.

When He'd gone, Adam turned to Eve and said, 'Well, you heard what He said, so let's get on with it! On your back, Woman, and brace yourself for a rattling good shag.'

And Eve spoke gently unto him, saying, 'I shall be your helpmeet and soulmate, your comfort and your wife. I shall cleave unto you and we shall be one flesh. But there will be no cleaving until you take that bloody stupid wig off.'

And all the while I pondered on His words regarding the apples on the tree, thinking that I had finally found the way to get my revenge on Him. My mind full of my plans, I left the Garden of Eden. But not before I'd watched Adam and Eve cleaving like rats up a drainpipe.

It was without doubt the most fun a log has ever had.[43]

43. We apologize for our apology at the beginning of the chapter. Having read these pages we now realize the title, 'Rude Bits', was an apt and accurate description of the subject matter contained herein. A bit saucy, wasn't it? We would further like make an apology to any reader who found the subject matter of this chapter offensive. We are very, very sorry – you must lead an incredibly dull life.

Chapter Twenty-One
The Temptation of Eve

good deal of nonsense has been written about my first great success. All this balderdash about me taking the form of a serpent, sidling up to Eve and hissing, 'Pssst! Wanna nibble my Cox?'

Complete fantasy, like so much in 'The Bible'. No self-respecting demon would conduct a temptation like that. Can you imagine the effect that a talking snake would have on a sensitive young woman? Scare her witless and have her running in the opposite direction, completely defeating the object of the exercise.

To be a great tempter you need to use psychology. First, you have to work out what you want to achieve. And then you contrive a simple but elegant plan to ensnare your victim.

In this case the object was to persuade Eve to take, eat and share the forbidden fruit with Adam. So what was the most natural and least suspicious way in which I could offer Eve an apple?

Exactly!

And so it came to pass that I set up my stall in Eden, posing as a Greengrocer and High Class Fruiterer. And a dashed good-looking one at that.

Basic psychology. After being cleaved round the clock by that short-arsed, bald-headed, turnip-brained, sex-crazed lout, she was only too ready to be tempted into accepting the gift of a juicy, rose-red apple from a handsome, suave charmer with a debonair moustache, roguish grin and twinkling eye.

It was as simple as that. Of course, I may also have casually mentioned that after eating the apple Adam would experience a severe limpness in the cleaving department.

Eve went skipping off to share her apple and I quietly left the Garden of Eden, pausing only to trample His hollyhocks.

Chapter Twenty-Two
The Cain Mutiny

ot even I realized just how easy it would be to alter the entire course of Himself's plans. The work of a few moments wrecked a millennium of His work. I knew He would be cross, but I little realized just how monumentally furious He would get over one small apple. His wrath was terrible to see. As soon as He learned of Adam and Eve's disobedience, He evicted them from Eden and forced them to wander, naked and alone, through the Earth, facing the terrors of the wilderness and the threats from ravening beasts, with nothing to comfort them except marathon cleaving sessions which were not much of a comfort for Eve who found she was increasingly suffering from headaches.

Things were pretty quiet, especially for me having only two people to tempt. This was proving futile as Eve was deaf to my blandishments, having sworn never, ever to talk to a stranger again. Adam was no better because only one thing tempted him and although I'm not noted for my squeamishness, even I drew the line at having carnal knowledge of someone who possessed all the charm, sensitivity and comeliness of a festering boil.

Unfortunately for her, Eve could not afford to be so choosy and so, despite a headache that lasted three years and seventeen days, the inevitable happened and she became pregnant.

Their first-born was Cain. As soon as I saw him I thought he was a promising little fellow and before he was toddling I was working on him, tempting him in every way I knew. Sadly without success. I couldn't persuade him to theft, as there was nothing in the world worth stealing. He was too young for adultery, even if Eve had been willing, which she wasn't because Cain was the spitting image of his father.

However, I did manage to get him to tell the odd lie – he would occasionally go up to Adam and say, 'Guess what, Dad! This morning I invented the wheel!'. When Adam asked what a wheel was and whether he could cleave the arse off it, Cain would say, 'I don't know! I was just making it up!' and run off chuckling to himself at his own naughtiness. It wasn't much – hardly the sort of transgression that would incur the wrath of Old Sourpuss Upstairs – but it was a start and I had high hopes for his future career.

These hopes were realized when, despite a headache lasting six years, five months and twelve days, Eve gave birth to her second son, Abel.

Cain didn't like Abel much because the younger boy was taller than him, had a full head of hair and had inherited his mother's good looks and gentility. He infuriated Cain by his fastidiousness in refusing to wear a goat's skin around him until it had first been separated from the goat.

One day, after Abel had been particularly prissy and complained about Cain urinating over some potatoes which, he said, was unhygienic, especially while he was eating them, Cain stormed off.

I found him sitting alone and, assuming the form of an itinerant Second-Hand Bits Of Wood Salesman, engaged him in conversation about the comparative merits of a large bit of wood with only one careful owner over a slightly bigger but cheaper bit of wood which had, admittedly, seen a certain amount of wear and tear.

After a lengthy debate, we agreed that the slightly bigger but cheaper bit of wood was, all things considered, preferable. We then haggled about the price until I allowed him to beat

me down to fifteen pebbles and a gerbil's jawbone. An incredible bargain, especially as I also agreed to take a twig in part exchange, but sometimes the end justifies the means.

Having concluded the deal, Cain went off, proudly cradling his new possession. Only to return a few minutes later, saying, 'Um. This large bit of wood I've just bought...what am I supposed to do with it?'

I explained to him that the bit of wood had magical properties and if used correctly would stop his brother criticizing him for his little foibles, like, for example, his habit of grabbing Abel by his testicles and squeezing them with all his might, which was the world's first and, at that time, only sporting activity.

'So,' he asked, 'how do I make this happen?'

'You simply take this large bit of wood and tap your brother on the head with it.'

'And what does that do?'

'If you tap hard enough, it...well, basically, it kills him.'

'Fine!'

Off he went again, humming happily.

A few minutes later he was back, saying, 'What exactly does "kills" mean?'

But by then I was no more than the merest wisp of sulphurous smoke.

Thus Abel became the world's first corpse. Cain became the world's first murderer. And Adam became the first person to fail to solve a whodunnit, lacking the intelligence to work out the culprit from a list of three suspects. Even when two of them had cast-iron alibis being, as he and Eve were, otherwise engaged in cleaving.

Cain's action enraged Old Misery Guts Upstairs who exiled him, forcing him to wander the desolate realms of Earth, searching in vain for a shrewd lawyer who could argue his innocence by proving that Abel had killed himself by repeatedly smashing his head against Cain's bit of wood.

It's doubtful that any lawyer, however sharp, could have convinced Himself that Abel was the world's first suicide. That record belongs to another of Adam's offspring, Clut, who I tempted into self-destruction by persuading him to jump from the top of a thousand-foot cliff, assuring him that the rocks below would break his fall. This was more difficult than I anticipated because I had trouble convincing Clut that when his body struck the rocks, it wouldn't do them any damage.

In the meantime Cain roamed the Earth for several hundred years until it finally dawned on Him that his quest for a lawyer was futile because even if he found one, he couldn't afford to pay him. This discovery caused him to lose the will to live.

I was more than pleased to welcome him as my very first client in Hades, where he has bided ever since, basking in the status of being our oldest and probably stupidest resident, with the exception of his brother Clut who is still full of remorse and tells anyone who listens, 'I can't forgive myself for making those lovely rocks all dirty with my blood.'

Since Cain's arrival we have been joined by countless billions more members, millions of whom have imitated and improved on his pioneering technique and who would willingly exercise them on Clut if only there was death after death.

Chapter Twenty-Three
The Dance of Death
Or
Apocalypso Now!

'm not one to boast, but within a very short space of time and at the expenditure of almost no effort, I had contrived the exile of Mankind from paradise and introduced murder.[44]

After that the going was easy. No sooner did Adam and Eve spawn a child than I tempted it to some new and delightful sin. For example, it was I who taught Onan the habit named after him.[45]

It was I who preached brotherly love. And sisterly love. Not to mention brotherly-in-law love and cousinly-once-removed love. It was I who encouraged Man to love his neighbour, especially when the neighbour's wife was out, experiencing total-strangerly love with whomsoever she happened to pick up. It was I who introduced the descendants of Adam to what

44. I'm lying again. I am, of course, one to boast. I even boast about my boastfulness. I am indubitably the most boastful being who has ever lived and that's being modest. Incredibly modest. In fact, I'm being so modest, I feel like boasting about it. But my incalculable and unequalled modesty prevents me.

128

CHAPTER TWENTY-THREE

Himself called the Seven Deadly Sins. I doubt whether anyone has ever enjoyed such job satisfaction.[46]

My successes were rapid and spectacular. As the world became populous, I rushed hither and thither, tempting, seducing, perverting and recruiting. Soon Hades was filling up with willing helpers, each of whom I sent out to spread my word and do my bidding, netting shoals of souls, diverting them from the straight and narrow, down the corkscrew path to my infernal realm.[47]

At this time, I reckoned I was claiming ten souls for every one who signed with Him. And as these members flocked to me, what did He do? He took to the bottle and drank Himself into an alcoholic daze lasting several thousand years.

As He slumbered in His drunken coma, Gabriel and the other archangels tried to staunch the flow of my subscribers

---

45. Onan's sin was self-abuse. He used to hurl insults at himself, shouting, 'I'm a deaf, blind, stunted, hairy-palmed tosser!' He believed himself to be completely insane, and blamed the condition on his new-found habit of spilling his seed on the ground. He was, in fact, completely insane but the cause of it was not self-gratification, but being dropped on his head by his brother, Er, who used the infant Onan as a ball which he kicked to his twin brother, Um.

   Er and Um were so called because when asked what names he would give them their father, Judah, an indecisive man, answered, 'Er... um...'. Yet another child was named Dunno for the same reason.

   Publisher's Note: This version does not coincide with that found in Genesis 38: 9, which states that Judah had only two sons: Er and Onan. Either we are privy to new and important information or The Author is lying through his teeth. We leave the reader to decide.

   A Doctor adds: 'There is no medical evidence to prove that Onanism makes you blind, deaf, hairy-palmed or stunts your growth. It certainly won't cause insanity. I practised the habit enthusiastically as a child and grew up to be as tall, clear-eyed and sane as the next emu.'

46. I also enjoyed considerable Job satisfaction, thanks to a particularly lissome youth of that name.

47. Being one to boast – see my incredibly fascinating Footnote 44 opposite, probably the most riveting footnote ever written – I'd just like to point out how poetic that paragraph is; indisputably the most poetic piece of prose ever penned. I'd further like to point out the pleasing alliteration of the phrase 'the most poetic piece of prose ever penned'.

   A Poet adds: 'Bollocks!'

but they battled in vain, there were so few of them and so many of us.

It couldn't last, of course. Eventually He sobered up, took a befuddled look at what was happening and decided to act. The action He took was absolutely typical. Suffering from the biggest and worst hangover in history, He went right over the top. His dipsomanic philosophy being, if you can't beat 'em, wipe 'em out.

CLAP!
FLASH!
PUFF!

A flood raced across the face of the Earth, total inundation, mass drownings – which rushed us off our feet down here – and only Noah and his holier-than-everyone family preserved.

So we started all over again. The first few generations of Noah's descendants were as goody-goody as he, but they soon got bored with living lives untainted by indulgence and, after a little first-rate tempting, they were taking to sin like Adam did to cleaving.

If anything they exceeded even Adam, especially the denizens of Sodom and Gomorrah who were probably my most enthusiastic converts and aptest pupils. Not only did the Sodomites and Gomorrans commit each and every one of Seven so-called Deadly Sins on a regular daily basis, they even invented an Eighth.[48]

Unfortunately, the fun to be had in Sodom and Gomorrah was short-lived. In an inexcusable burst of alcoholic ill-

48. In addition to Pride, Anger, Envy, Lust, Gluttony, Greed and Sloth, the Sodomites and Gomorrans occasionally committed the heinous sin of Globbery, a practice so vile and disgusting that it even repulsed the people who performed it. Personally, I only tried it once and found it mildly pleasurable, considerably more pleasurable than my partner who, as a result, was struck both dumb and doubly incontinent and was never able to play the zither again. I was never able to indulge in Globbery after that because by the time the sores had healed and the swelling on my pancreas had subsided, the world's entire supply of unicorns – without which any small thrill received from Globbery was impossible – had been wiped out in the holocaust that struck the twin cities.

temper The Old Moaner obliterated them from the Earth, saving only Lot, a miserable curmudgeon whose idea of having a good time was to write to *The Sodom Times* suggesting that his fellow citizens had their sexual organs either cut off or sewn up. And, in the case of some of my more enthusiastic and less discriminating acolytes, both.

Still, I got my revenge on Lot by creeping up behind his wife as they were fleeing the city, tapping her on the shoulder and whispering, 'Bet you've never seen one as big as this before!'. Naturally, she couldn't overcome her curiosity and turned to take a surreptitious peek.[49]

For this minor misdemeanour Himself instantly turned her into a pillar of salt, which I later carved into the shape of an immense phallus as a monument to those fun-loving folk who gave the world some of its most pleasurable sexual practices. This thrusting edifice became the Ninth Wonder of The World to which millions flocked, gazing in awe at its towering rigidity and gasping, 'Verily, this is an amazing erection! It makes The Colossus of Rhodes look like he's suffering from brewer's droop!'[50]

It was typical of His over-reaction to raze entire cities to the ground just because the people living in them knew how to enjoy themselves and, indeed, each other. When I think of all the things I've been blamed for, they pale into insignificance against what He's done in a fit of pique. How many towns have I ever obliterated? Well, admittedly there were one or two minor metropoli but they were just mistakes. That unfortunate business at Pompeii, for example. A simple error that anyone could make. There I was one day, patronizing one of its many excellent whorehouses, spreading a few of the more

49. Let this be a lesson to the sanctimonious among you. It is very unwise to say, 'Get thee behind me, Satan!'. Especially when I'm feeling randy. Which is all the time.

50. It has always been believed that there were only Seven Wonders of the Ancient World. The Author claims that the Phallus of Sodom was the Ninth and that the Eighth was the Hanging Baskets of Nineveh which although less impressive in sheer size than The Hanging Gardens of Babylon were generally agreed by experts to contain far prettier trailing lobelia. (In the publishers' opinion, this whole story should be taken with a pillar of salt.)

virulent venereal diseases, when I eavesdropped a customer asking his harlot, 'Did the earth move for you?'. Hearing her say it didn't, I thought I'd help out. Trouble is, I sometimes forget my own power. Pity about Pompeii, it was shaping up to be my kind of town.

So was San Francisco, until the earthquake in 1906. Of course, it's been blamed on the San Andreas Fault. Rubbish! The fault was entirely mine. I only meant to hit it with a minor tremor, just to shake things up a bit and cause some amusing panic and confusion. Instead, I somewhat overdid it. Oh, well, not to worry. It was soon rebuilt and is back in business as a pleasure centre. At least temporarily.[51]

However, I will not take the blame for every disaster that strikes the Earth. I had nothing whatsoever to do with The Black Death. Plagues have never been among my favoured catastrophes, there's no fun and little profit in them. To find the culprit, look Upstairs. Plagues are His speciality – locusts, frogs, boils, He's supplied them all.

And look what He did to the first-born of Egypt – slew the lot of them! Such profligate waste! He may be omnipotent but He lacks style. And He's short-sighted – an astute business-man, like myself, doesn't massacre a generation. What you need is some forward planning – I'd have spared the grubby little brats so that later I could lead them astray and they'd mature into first-rate trouble-makers.

Such subtleties are completely lost on Him. He sticks to His old-fashioned ways – chastizing and smiting, purging and decimating, summoning up plagues and pestilences with a click of His fingers, laying waste to perfectly good tracts of real estate with fire, flood and thunderbolt.

All that carnage and slaughter, and the extraordinary thing is that He's got away with it for five thousand years!

51. That's got you San Franciscans worried, hasn't it? Just teasing! You're safe for a while. I won't tell you exactly how long but if any of you are planning to read *War and Peace*, get started on it as soon as you've finished this book. Incidentally, to those of you living in nearby Los Angeles, who may also be worried about the imminence of an earth-quake, I just say this – I hope you're enjoying my book, and although it is drawing towards its brilliant conclusion, have you ever thought of taking a speed-reading course?

CHAPTER TWENTY-THREE

Not only that but people worship Him for it! It's enough to drive me to Tee-Totalism.

Don't the fools who venerate Him realize that He's past it? Ga-ga! Far too senile for the job. It's time He made way for a younger Supreme Being, someone with drive, energy, ideas, marketing skills, the ability to read the bottom line and do some astute number-crunching, soul-wise.

Just imagine what things would be like if I was in charge!

Chapter Twenty-Four
Let Pandemonium Reign!

 f I ruled the world, *when* I rule the world, the first thing I will do is issue My One Commandment.

THOU SHALT DO WHAT THE HELL YOU LIKE!

After that anything goes!

And the first to go will be Christmas, Easter and every other festival associated with the usurped pretender and his son. Then we will defrock all his priests and strip his nuns, parading them naked through the thronging streets to be tormented and abused by My howling, blood-crazed mobs.

Heretics who refuse to recant their errant beliefs and abase themselves before My majesty will be subjected to lingering deaths of unimaginable agony at the hands of My followers. And the hounds of Hell will feast upon their flesh.

Then the revels will commence! Lust and greed, anger and gluttony will be unleashed as the world cavorts to the frenzied tattoo of My demonic drumbeat!

All will be chaos and pandemonium, over which I, The Lord

of Misrule, will preside as each of you prances and capers to do My diabolic bidding.

Join Me and all this will come to pass. Together we will create Hell on earth!

And Mine will be the kingdom and the power and the glory! For ever and ev...

CLAP!

*

FLASH!

*

PUFF!

Croak!

CHAPTER TWENTY-FOUR

**Due to circumstances beyond his control, the author has unexpectedly been forced to abandon this manuscript.
Any reader wishing to contact the author may address correspondence to:**

MURIEL TOAD, ESQ.,
THE THIRD LILYPAD FROM THE LEFT,
THE DUCK POND,
EREWHON,
THE SPACE – TIME CONTINUUM.

AMEN!

PS. In My trade we call this a 'Deus ex machina'. All it took was one click of My fingers. Not bad for a senile, alcoholic dwarf in a ginger toupée.

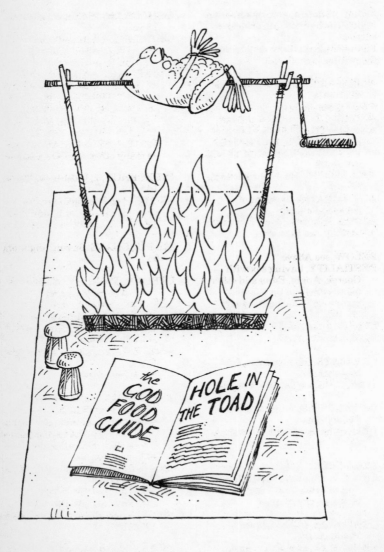

SINDEX

Figures in *italic* denote illustrations.
Figures in **bold** denote principal entries.
Figures in ***bold italic*** denote that the printer is confused.

AARDVARK, as a sexual aid, see Bestiality
ABOVE, see Below
ANGER 3, 7, *13*, 48. See also Ire
ANIMAL THAT LOOKS LIKE A HEARTH RUG AND HANGS UPSIDE DOWN FROM TREES, see Sloth
ART, EROTIC, see illustrations pp. *55–64*
ART, ERRATIC, see work of Jackson Pollack
AURAL SEX, see Zones, Erroneous
AVARICE, see Rice, Ava

BELOW, see Above
BESTIALITY, having sex with George, Angie, Edna and other members of the Best family including Fluff the Aardvark; 99, 102, *121*
BORGE, Lucrezia, *57*
BORGIA, Victor, *88*

CATAMITE, 64; Dogamite, 65; Marmite, 66
CONDOMS, see Letters, French

DEADLY SINS, 7. See also Seven Deadly Sins
DRUGS, hard, 45; soft, 47; wobbly, 49

ELSEWHERE, see Seven Dwarfs
ENVY, 4; Jealousy, 12. (Jealousy won in extra time.) See also Monster, Green-eyed

GENITALIA, FEMALE, see Maidenhead
GENITALIA, MALE, see inside trousers

GOMORRAH, The Sin of, see Sink Tidies
GLOBBERY, 22; its influence on the Metaphysical Poets, 0
GLUTTONY, see Greed
GREED, 1, 4, 9, 10, *11*, 14, 19, 20, 21, 22, *23*, 24, 26, 28, 30–38, *40*, 44, 45, 47, 50–62, 64, 66, 73, 77, 80, *83–85*, 90, 91, 93, 95, 96, 97, 98, 99, 100, 103–106, *108*, 111, 115, 118, 120, 124, 125, 127, 129–131, *132*, 140, 144, 151 and as many other pages as possible.

INDECENCY, 1; Indecency, Gross, 144
INSECT, sexual relations with member of one's own family, 45; possibility that it's a misprint of 'incest', *97*
IRE PURCHASE, buying anger on, 94

LETTERS, FRENCH – é and ç – 27; see also Letters, Greek
LETTERS, GREEK – αβΩδ – the rudest word in the world, 77; see also W*********k, the rudest word in the universe.
LINGUS, Cunni, *69*; see also Lingus, Aer
LUST, 1–298, passim

MAIDENHEAD, town on River Thames near Windsor, Berkshire, England; population (1981) 49,038. Not to be confused with female genitalia, and seldom is, 34
MASTURBATION, harmful effects of, see Myopia
MONSTER, GREEN-EYED, 86; blue-eyed, 88; one-eyed, 89
MYOPIA, see an optician, but with difficulty

NERO, and the dangers of barbecues, 139

RECOMMENDED READING

In the light of what has befallen The Author, the publishers
would strongly recommend the reader to 'The Bible', both Old
and New Testaments.

ALSO RECOMMENDED

The Book of Common Prayer
Hymns Ancient and Modern

NOT RECOMMENDED

Other works by The Author, especially:
'Teach Yourself Alkemy'
'Teach Yourself Neckromancy'
'Teach Yourself Sorsery'
'Teach Yourself Speling'

ERRATA

The Publishers apologize for the many errors of fact that riddle this work.

We would most particularly like to apologize for the most grievous mistake of all – ever having published it.

The Managing Director would like to apologize and take full responsibility. He particularly regrets that being, as he now is, a small brown stain, the result of a well-directed thunderbolt, he is unable to do this personally.

THE F!_l END